Teacher Guide

Passwords
Science Vocabulary

Developers: Joan Krensky and Maureen Devine Sotoohi

Cover Design: Susan Hawk

Photo Credits: Front cover: Courtesy of NASA

Product Development and Design: Chameleon Publishing Services
Written by Barbara Klemetti Mindell

Reviewers: Curriculum Associates, LLC would like to acknowledge the contribution of the educators who reviewed *Passwords: Science Vocabulary* at various stages of its development. Their insightful comments have made our program a better one for teachers and students.

Gracie Alvear
Bilingual/ESL/Immigrant Student Service
Elementary Supervisor
Edinburg CISD
Edinburg, Texas

Rebecca Braaten
Secondary Science Senior Coordinator
Instructional Services Division
Polk County Schools
Bartow, Florida

Jackie Baldwin
Secondary Reading Senior Coordinator
Instructional Services Division
Polk County Schools
Bartow, Florida

Lorraine Cruz
Principal
Ames Middle School
Chicago, Illinois

Leonila Izaguirre
Bilingual-ESL Director
Pharr-San Juan-Alamo ISD
Pharr, Texas

Judy Lewis
Director, State and Federal Programs
Folsom Cordova Unified School District
Folsom, California

Dominique Mongeau
Categorical Program Adviser
Carson Street Elementary School
Los Angeles Unified School District
Carson, California

Connie Shaffer
Instructional Development Services
Orange County Public Schools
Orlando, Florida

Science Content Reviewer
Jonathan Schwartz
Earth Science Teacher
West Hartford Public Schools
West Hartford, Connecticut

Curriculum Associates

Table of Contents

ISBN 978-0-7609-4305-2
©2007—Curriculum Associates, LLC
North Billerica, MA 01862

15 14 13 12 11 10 9 8 7 6 5 4

Passwords: Science Vocabulary is designed to build the vocabulary essential to understanding the key concepts students are studying in science. The topic areas and vocabulary words used in *Passwords: Science Vocabulary* have been chosen based on the National Science Education Standards and the science standards developed by individual states. The topics and vocabulary words also align with the basal science textbooks of major publishers.

The *Passwords: Science Vocabulary* program consists of eight books, Levels A through H, as well as individual **Earth Science, Life Science,** and **Physical Science** books designed for use by older students.

Passwords: Science Vocabulary is recommended for all students who need practice with the vocabulary that will help them succeed in science. These students may include English language learners as well as other striving learners. See pages 9–11 of this teacher guide for vocabulary teaching strategies that will help teachers meet the needs of all their students.

While the lessons in *Passwords: Science Vocabulary* are grouped by topic area, each lesson may be taught independently. For a broad introduction to science, teachers may go through the book lesson by lesson. Alternatively, teachers may use only the lessons related to the science topic being taught in class. By providing an overview of grade-appropriate science topics, *Passwords: Science Vocabulary* may also be used to help students prepare and review for standardized tests in science.

The *Passwords: Science Vocabulary* student book reading selections are available on an audio CD. The CD is a useful tool to use with English language learners or other students who would benefit from listening to the reading selections multiple times. Auditory learners will find listening to the selections on the CD especially helpful.

 **CA101®** Online e-training   Use this product right away, the right way!
Online e-training at **CAtraining.com**

Passwords: Science Vocabulary student books have been written and designed to provide students with a text that is "considerate," or reader friendly. Three hallmarks of considerate text are: clear text structure, coherent writing, and audience appropriateness. **Passwords: Science Vocabulary** incorporates these characteristics of considerate text into every lesson.

Text Structure

The reading selections in **Passwords: Science Vocabulary** feature text structures that exhibit clear organizational patterns. In descriptive text, information is given in a logical order of importance. For sequential text, events are presented in the order in which they occur. In cause-and-effect text, the relation between the actions or events is clearly stated.

Coherent Writing

The science concepts and ideas presented in **Passwords: Science Vocabulary** are clearly stated. An introductory paragraph states the topic of the lesson. All the information in the reading selection connects to the topic. No extraneous material confuses readers. Headings and subheads highlight the cohesion of each text segment. Transitional words and phrases signal the relation between actions or concepts.

Audience Appropriateness

Although the readability of **Passwords: Science Vocabulary** reading selections is below grade level, the concepts and material in the passages are grade appropriate. Prereading activities activate students' prior knowledge. Activities that follow the reading selection help teachers evaluate student understanding.

Look for these signs of considerate text in the **Passwords: Science Vocabulary** student books.

- Short line length for increased readability
- Simple sentence structure
- Paragraphs with clear topic sentences and relevant supporting details
- Introductory subheads
- Target vocabulary words boldfaced in text
- Definitions of target vocabulary words near the first use of the word
- Simple font
- Clean page layout
- Appropriate, not overwhelming, visuals
- Illustrations support content

Each student book for Earth Science, Life Science, and Physical Science has 15 lessons. Each lesson introduces and practices ten key vocabulary words related to a single science topic.

Features of the Lesson

Each lesson of the student book contains these features:

- Target Vocabulary
- Lesson Opener
- Reading Selection
- Graphics
- Activities A–D
- Word Root
- Write!

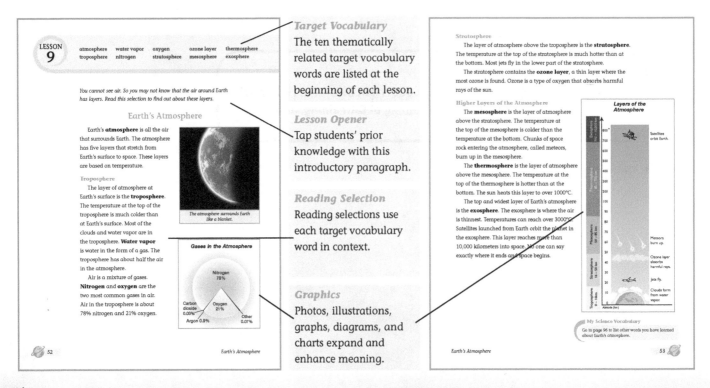

Target Vocabulary
The ten thematically related target vocabulary words are listed at the beginning of each lesson.

Lesson Opener
Tap students' prior knowledge with this introductory paragraph.

Reading Selection
Reading selections use each target vocabulary word in context.

Graphics
Photos, illustrations, graphs, diagrams, and charts expand and enhance meaning.

Progressively difficult activities follow each reading selection.

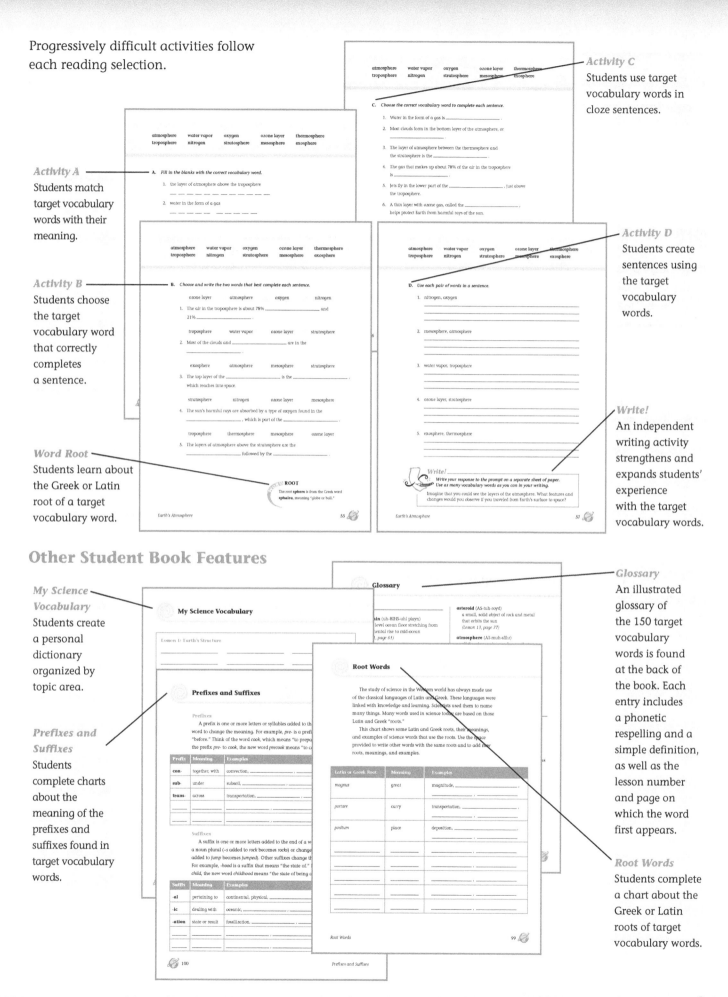

Activity A
Students match target vocabulary words with their meaning.

Activity B
Students choose the target vocabulary word that correctly completes a sentence.

Word Root
Students learn about the Greek or Latin root of a target vocabulary word.

Activity C
Students use target vocabulary words in cloze sentences.

Activity D
Students create sentences using the target vocabulary words.

Write!
An independent writing activity strengthens and expands students' experience with the target vocabulary words.

Other Student Book Features

My Science Vocabulary
Students create a personal dictionary organized by topic area.

Prefixes and Suffixes
Students complete charts about the meaning of the prefixes and suffixes found in target vocabulary words.

Glossary
An illustrated glossary of the 150 target vocabulary words is found at the back of the book. Each entry includes a phonetic respelling and a simple definition, as well as the lesson number and page on which the word first appears.

Root Words
Students complete a chart about the Greek or Latin roots of target vocabulary words.

Teacher Guide

The Teacher Guide for **Passwords: Science Vocabulary** contains resources that may be used to introduce, support, and extended students' science vocabulary studies. The Teacher Guide includes guided instruction for each student-book lesson.

Multi-Step Lesson Plan

Passwords: Science Vocabulary is built upon the premise that students benefit most from the direct instruction of vocabulary. Each lesson as presented in the Teacher Guide follows a multi-step lesson plan.

1. Introduction of the target vocabulary
2. Activation of students' prior knowledge
3. Provision of the meaning of unknown words
4. Creation by students of visual representations using graphic organizers
5. Further experiences with the target vocabulary
6. Activities that help students retain the word and its meaning

Listening, Speaking, Reading, and Writing

Passwords: Science Vocabulary provides opportunities for students to practice the target vocabulary words while listening, speaking, reading, and writing. These icons indicate opportunities for students to use the vocabulary words in different domains.

 Listening

 Speaking

 Reading

 Writing

Features of the Guided Teaching Lessons

Each lesson of the Teacher Guide contains these features:

- Target Vocabulary with definitions
- Cognates
- Vocabulary Strategy
- Lesson Summary
- Before Reading
- Word and Definition Cards
- Reproduced student book pages
- During Reading
- After Reading
- Annotated student book activity pages
- Extensions
- Ideas for introducing the Write! activity
- Sample answer for Write!
- Word Root extension

Target Vocabulary
The ten target vocabulary words are listed here with convenient, student-friendly definitions.

Cognates
Cognates can be a powerful tool in developing the vocabulary of English language learners.

Vocabulary Strategy
A vocabulary strategy that is particularly appropriate for the lesson is highlighted here.

Word and Definition Cards
Teacher Guide page references make it easy to find and use the word and definition cards.

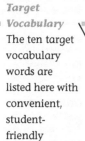
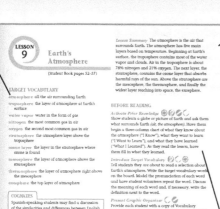

Lesson Summary
Use the summary for a quick introduction to the topic of the lesson.

Reproduced Student Book Pages
Student book lessons are reproduced for easy reference.

Before Reading
Questions and activities activate student's prior knowledge, build background, and motivate students to read. Graphic organizers are provided to build students' understanding of the target vocabulary words.

During Reading
Includes suggestions for presenting the reading selection and tips for explaining possibly difficult or confusing target vocabulary words.

After Reading
Provides guidance in using the graphic organizers to sum up the lesson and reminders to direct students to My Science Vocabulary and the Glossary.

Activities
The reproduced student book activity pages are annotated.

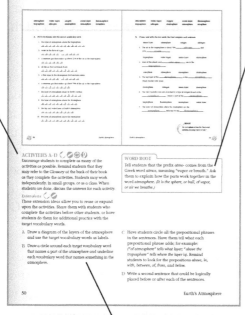

Word Root
Provides additional information about the student book Word Root.

Write!
Each guided lesson provides hints about presenting the Write! activity as well as a sample answer.

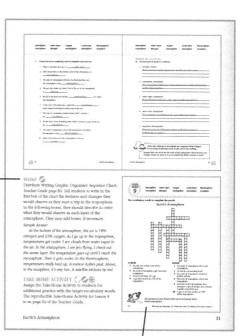

Extensions
An extension idea for each student book activity allows the activities to be reused or expanded.

Take-Home Activity
The Take-Home Activity for the lesson is reproduced with the answers provided.

Other Teacher Guide Features

- **Vocabulary Teaching Strategies**
  Information and tips about how to employ vocabulary teaching strategies that have proven effective with struggling learners and English language learners begin on page 9.

- **Research Summary**
  A summary of the research that forms the basis of **Passwords: Science Vocabulary** is on pages 12–15.

- **Reproducibles**
  Pages 76–128 of the Teacher Guide contain reproducibles for you to share with students.

  ### Graphic Organizers
  You may either photocopy the graphic organizers for students to use or use the sample graphic organizer as a model for students to create their own. The Before Reading section of each guided lesson suggests a particular vocabulary graphic organizer to use with the lesson. The Write! section of each guided lesson suggests a writing graphic organizer to use with the Write! activity.

  - **Vocabulary Graphic Organizers**

    Word Web   Students write a topic in the central circle. Then they group related target vocabulary words in the outer circles. Beside each circle, they write a phrase that explains why they grouped the words together.

    Venn Diagram   Students title each circle of the Venn Diagram with a topic. Then they categorize the target vocabulary words under the appropriate title, writing words that belong under both titles in the overlap of the circles.

    Four Square   In this graphic organizer, students write a target vocabulary word or a topic in the center rectangle. They label the surrounding squares with heads that relate to the word or topic. Then they write information about the word or topic under the appropriate head.

    Cycle   Students use this graphic organizer for information about science cycles. They write a topic in the center of the organizer and add the target vocabulary words in the appropriate places around the circle.

  - **Writing Graphic Organizers**

    Main Idea and Details Chart   This graphic organizer may be used with a variety of writing assignments. Students write a main idea in one box and the details that support it in another box.

    Idea Wheel   This variation of a web can be used with different types of writing. Students write a topic or main idea in the center of the wheel. On the spokes of the wheel, they add details or ideas about the topic or main idea.

    Narrative Map   Use this graphic organizer when students are asked to write a narrative. They record the character(s) and setting(s) in the top boxes and the events of the narrative in the bottom box.

    Sequence Chart   A sequence chart provides students with a visual representation of the steps in a process. In this organizer, they record the steps, in order, in a series of boxes.

  ### Word and Definition Cards
  Word cards for each target vocabulary word as well as cards with the definitions for the words are on pages 99–128 of this Teacher Guide. You may either cut the cards out of the book or photocopy them, cut them apart, and then use them. For ideas on how to use the word and definition cards, see page 10 of this Teacher Guide.

  ### Take-Home Activities
  Each student book lesson has a take-home activity for additional practice and an opportunity for students to share what they have learned with family members.

Vocabulary Teaching Strategies

These teaching strategies have been shown to be effective with English language learners, but all students who are studying vocabulary will find them helpful.

Accessing Prior Knowledge

Like their English-speaking peers, English language learners come to the classroom with a large body of knowledge. The challenge as a teacher of English language learners is tapping into this knowledge. Before introducing a lesson topic, ask students what they already know about the subject. By doing this, you not only acknowledge students' experiences, but you also find out what information and misinformation students have about the topic. This will enable you to plan a more relevant and focused lesson. Each student book lesson of **Passwords: Science Vocabulary** begins with an introductory paragraph written to tap into students' prior knowledge and to provide motivation for reading. In addition, this Teacher Guide includes a prior knowledge activity for each lesson.

Picture File

Use magazines or Web sources to create a file of pictures for each science topic. Students will enjoy looking for pictures and pasting them to construction paper. Use the pictures to illustrate target vocabulary words or key concepts. Pictures can be used before, during, or after reading in matching games, gallery walks, and as writing prompts.

Graphic Organizers

This Teacher Guide includes four vocabulary graphic organizers and four writing graphic organizers that can be reproduced for use by students. (See pages 76–83.)

Vocabulary graphic organizers can provide students with a visual representation of a word's meaning by showing examples, synonyms, drawings, descriptions, or the definition of the word. Students can add to the graphic organizer as their understanding of the word increases.

Writing graphic organizers help students organize their thoughts and plan their writing. The writing graphic organizers included in this Teacher Guide are intended for use with different kinds of Write! activities.

Total Physical Response

Total Physical Response, or TPR, is a language-teaching method first developed by Dr. James Asher, a professor of psychology. Asher based his method on his observations of how children learn their native language. In TPR, teachers replace parents, modeling verbal commands, while students respond physically. As a language-teaching method, TPR emphasizes listening and physical response over written language. It has been found to be an effective method for teaching vocabulary. In using TPR to teach vocabulary, teachers and students use movement to associate a word with its meaning. For example, to teach the target vocabulary word *rotate*, have your students get up and turn around. To teach the word *orbit*, have students walk around an object placed in the center of the classroom. To use TPR in your classroom, give commands that require a physical response from students. When they are ready, students can reverse roles, giving commands to you and to fellow students.

Context Clues

Students need to be directly instructed on how to use context clues to help them figure out the meaning of unknown words. There are several different kinds of context clues.

- **Definition**
  In this type of context clue, a definition, or restatement, of the unknown word is provided in the text. Words that signal a definition context clue include *means, refers to,* or *is*. Definition context clues are frequently used in **Passwords: Science Vocabulary**.

- **Synonym**
  Writers sometimes use familiar words with similar meanings to build meaning for an unknown or unfamiliar word.

- **Example**
  Point out to students that writers will sometimes provide an example that will help them figure out the meaning of an unfamiliar word. Words that may signal an example include *like, these, for example,* and *such as*.

Cognates

Cognates are words in different languages that resemble one another in both sound and meaning. Spanish and English have many cognates, especially in the area of science where words in both languages draw upon Latin and Greek roots. Some cognates are spelled identically, although pronunciation differs; for example the words *capital, tractor,* and *radio.* Others are spelled similarly; *rayo* and *ray.* Other words that seem similar are not cognates at all. *Bigote* does not mean "bigot"; it means "mustache."

Teachers cannot assume that Spanish-speaking students will automatically or correctly connect an English word with a Spanish cognate. To help students develop the ability to recognize cognates, each **Passwords: Science Vocabulary** Teacher Guide lesson includes a list of the Spanish cognates for the target vocabulary in that lesson. As you discuss these cognates with students, point out spelling patterns, such as *-tion* (English) and *-ción* (Spanish). This will help students develop generalizations about language patterns and enhance their ability to use their knowledge of their native language to learn English. Encourage your Spanish-speaking students to guess at the meaning of words in English based on their knowledge of Spanish. If you read the selections aloud, ask Spanish speakers to indicate when they think they hear a cognate. If students read the selections themselves, have them write down the words they think might be cognates. Discuss possible cognates when students have finished reading the selection. Write the word pairs on the board and have students come to the board and circle the similarities between the two words. Have students look for patterns. Students who speak languages other than Spanish may also be able to find English cognates of words from their native languages.

Greek and Latin Roots

Introducing the study of Greek and Latin roots to students who are learning English may initially seem to be adding another layer of difficulty to language learning. However, students who speak a romance language (Spanish, French, Italian, Portuguese, Romanian) will often find that the Latin or Greek root of an English word is similar to a word they know in their own language. Students who speak Haitian Creole may find that their native language, which draws heavily upon French, also has many links to Latin.

When teaching students how to use roots to determine word meaning, remind them that many long English words are made up of smaller parts. The root of the word is the part that contains the most important aspect of the word's meaning. For example, if students come across the word *astronomy* and they recognize the root *astro* from their study of Greek and Latin roots and they remember that the root *astro* is related to star, they can begin to figure out that *astronomy* has something to do with stars.

Students will find a chart of Greek and Latin roots, with examples of target vocabulary words that have those roots, on page 99 of the student book.

Prefixes and Suffixes

A prefix is a word part that is attached to the beginning of a base word. A suffix is a word part that is attached to the end of a base word. The meaning of a prefix or suffix combines with the meaning of the base word. For example, the prefix *tri-,* meaning "three," combines with *angle* to form *triangle,* a figure with three angles. The suffix *-ward,* meaning "in the direction of," combines with *back* to form *backward.* Knowing the meaning of common prefixes and suffixes is another tool students can use to help them figure out the meaning of unknown words and remember the meaning of words they are learning.

Students will find a chart of common prefixes and suffixes, with examples of target vocabulary words that have these prefixes or suffixes, on page 100 of the student book.

Word Cards

This Teacher Guide includes reproducible word and definition cards on pages 99–128. Each page contains one lesson's words or definitions. These cards can be used in teacher-led activities, and small group activities, to introduce new vocabulary, and to review vocabulary and concepts. Word cards are helpful to visual, kinesthetic, and aural learners. Word cards provide students with visual cues and constant reinforcement. Many word card activities require you to create copies of the cards. You can photocopy the cards on cardstock or on plain paper. If you want to use the cards as flashcards, with the definition on the back, photocopy the pages as two-sided copies. For many activities, however, you will need cards with one blank side and the word or the definition on the other side. After you make the copies, cut the cards apart. Store the cards in labeled plastic zipper bags for easy access. If you want to provide each student with a set of cards, you might consider having students create their own cards using blank 3½" × 5" file cards. Although you will certainly come up with many ideas of how to use these cards on your own, here are a few activities to begin with.

- **Word Wall**

  A Word Wall can be a great tool in helping students learn vocabulary. Although words are generally displayed on a bulletin board, you can also use more portable display surfaces, such as a shower curtain or a trifold board. Add words to the Word Wall as you introduce the target vocabulary. Review the words daily. Change the words as you begin a new lesson. Word Walls lend themselves to a variety of activities.

  ### Five Clues

  Have each student number their paper from one to five. Give a clue about one of the words on the Word Wall. Students should write down the word they think you are thinking of. Keep giving clues (up to five) until everyone has guessed the word you were thinking of.

  ### Lights On!

  You'll need a flashlight for this activity. Turn off the classroom lights. Then point the flashlight at one word on the Word Wall. Call on a student to read the word and either use it in a sentence or provide the definition. When the student is successful, it is his or her turn to point the flashlight at a word and choose another student to read the word.

  ### Wordo

  Provide each student with a bingo-type grid with six blank spaces. Tell students to fill in the blanks with words from the Word Wall. Put the corresponding definition cards into a jar. Pull the definition cards from the jar one by one. Read the definition and have students cover the corresponding word on their grid with a marker. When the entire card is covered, Wordo!

- **Card Games**

  The word cards can be used in many different card games, some of which are variations of games played with regular playing cards. Here are a few ideas for games using the word cards.

  ### Concentration

  The object of this game is to find matching pairs. Prepare two sets of cards. One set of cards has the target vocabulary words and the other set has the definitions. Prepare from 10 cards (for 5 matches) to 30 cards (15 matches). Mix up the two sets of cards. Place the cards face down in rows. Players take turns turning over pairs of cards. If the cards match, the player makes a sentence using the vocabulary word. If the cards don't match, play goes to the next player. If the student successfully creates a sentence using the vocabulary word, he or she goes again. The player with the most cards at the end is the winner.

  ### Guess the Word

  This game is for four students, playing in pairs. Prepare a card for each target vocabulary word. Put the cards face down in the middle of the table. The first student of the first pair picks a card and gives a one-word clue to his or her partner that will enable the partner to guess the vocabulary word. If the partner does not guess the word, the word goes to a member of the other pair who gives a hint to his or her partner. The team that successfully guesses the word keeps the card. The team with the most cards wins.

What Is the Need for *Passwords: Science Vocabulary*?

The curriculum area of science has been receiving increased attention at both the federal and state levels. Several initiatives have focused the educational spotlight onto science education, resulting in increased demand for improved instruction and student achievement. Some active programs and initiatives that are creating a need for academic science vocabulary instruction are:

- The NCLB Act of 2001 requires states to assess students' progress in science at least once in each of these three grade spans (3–5, 6–9, 10–12) each year, starting in 2007.

- "English language learners (ELLs) who experience slow vocabulary development are less able to comprehend text at grade level than their English-only peers. Such students are likely to perform poorly on assessments in these areas and are at risk of being diagnosed as learning disabled" (August, Carlo, Dressler, & Snow, 2005).

- American Competitiveness Initiative—In 2006, President Bush's education agenda is concentrating on strengthening America's educational system in the areas of STEM (science, technology, engineering, and mathematics). This initiative is currently affecting high school curriculum. However, schools may start preparing for this initiative in elementary and middle school.

The educational spotlight will continue to focus on math and science education as accountability deadlines approach and as initiatives are finalized. *Passwords: Science Vocabulary* unites students with a singular goal of successfully learning the academic language of science. This goal is attainable through the instructional features and strategies that research has proven to be effective with diverse student populations.

Why Is *Passwords: Science Vocabulary* Helpful to ELL Students?

Academic Language Proficiency is the ability of the student to comprehend, speak, read, and write when the context is reduced and the topic is cognitively demanding. Examples of cognitively demanding activities are reading textbooks, writing long compositions, learning new concepts, and mastering local and state requirements that test students on the academic language of each content area. Zelasko & Antunez (2000) state that "without mastery of classroom English, they [ELL students] will have difficulty competing academically in an all-English setting." The importance of learning academic language is confirmed by additional researchers:

- "Vocabulary development is one of the greatest challenges to reading instruction for ELLs, because in order to read fluently and comprehend what is written, students need to use not just phonics, but context" (Antunez, 2002).

- "For English language learners, academic English is like a third language, their second language being the social English of the hallways, community, and media. And whereas students are exposed to social English in various settings, academic language acquisition is generally limited to the classroom. . . . Many English language learners, even those with well-developed social language, struggle to master the complex language of school" (Zwiers, 2004/2005).

What Are the Strategies and Features in *Passwords: Science Vocabulary* that Research Has Proven to Be Effective with ELL Students?

Science is a cognitively demanding school subject. The first step to comprehending the content of a school subject is to understand the vocabulary and language of the school subject. ***Passwords: Science Vocabulary*** incorporates ELL instructional recommendations from content-area experts for teaching vocabulary.

Marzano & Pickering (2005), in *Building Academic Vocabulary*, promotes a six-step process for teaching new terms. This process is also integrated in ***Passwords: Science Vocabulary***.

Step 1: Provide a description, an explanation, or an example of the new term (along with a nonlinguistic representation).

Step 2: Ask students to restate the description, explanation, or example in their own words.

Step 3: Ask students to construct a picture, symbol, or graphic representing the term or phrase.

Step 4: Engage students periodically in activities that help them add to their knowledge of the terms.

Step 5: Engage students periodically to discuss the terms with one another.

Step 6: Involve students periodically in games that allow them to play with terms.

Additionally, educational experts and researchers from numerous professional organizations (National Science Teachers Association, English Language Summit), have created a list of instructional recommendations that have been found to be effective, especially with ELL students. While these organizations are separate entities, they share some common recommendations. These recommendations are integrated throughout ***Passwords: Science Vocabulary***.

***Passwords: Science Vocabulary* Uses . . .**	**Research Says . . .**
Direct Instruction within Context (SB, Reading Passage & Activities A–D)	*"The teaching of individual words is most effective when learners are given both definitional and contextual information, when learners actively process the new word meanings, and when they experience multiple encounters with words" (Graves & Watts-Taffe, 2002).* *"It is important to teach vocabulary within the scientific context, not in isolation" (NSTA, 2006).*
Prior-knowledge Activation (SB, Prereading Activity; TG)	*"Students who lack in academic background knowledge also lack in academic achievement. To be most effective, a teacher should be aware of each student's level of background knowledge" (Marzano & Pickering, 2005).* *"To facilitate communication of content knowledge, teachers can offer support in several ways: Plan adequate time to activate students' prior knowledge and encourage students to share what they already know in journals, small groups, or paired brainstorming sessions" (Rolón, 2002/2003).*
Collaborative Learning (SB, Prereading Activity & Activities A–D; TG)	*"Students interacting verbally with other native speakers of English pick up vocabulary and content knowledge" (English Language Summit, 2004).* *"Research and common sense . . . confirm that interacting with other people about what we are learning deepens the understanding of everyone involved—particularly when we are learning new terms" (Marzano & Pickering, 2005).*
Differentiated Instruction (SB, Activities A–D; TG)	*"Because children differ, no single text nor any single task can be appropriate for all children in a classroom . . ." (Allington, 2005).* *"Numerous theorists and contemporary translators of brain research propose that students do not learn effectively when tasks are too simple or too complex for their particular readiness levels. Rather, say these researchers, tasks must be moderately challenging for the individual for growth to occur" (Tomlinson, 2004).*
Parental Engagement (TG, Take-Home Activities)	*"The evidence is consistent, positive, and convincing: families have a major influence on their children's achievement in school and through life" (National Center for Family & Community Connections with Schools, 2002).*
Total Physical Response (TG, Vocabulary Teaching Strategies section, During Reading Activity)	*"Having children physically act out songs, poems, or readings—all forms of TPR methodology—is an effective way to support vocabulary development" (Drucker, 2003).* *In a research synthesis, Slavin & Cheung (2005) state that teachers of English language learners may use language development strategies, such as total physical response, to help students internalize new vocabulary.*
Considerate Text (SB, Reading Passages)	*"Certain features of text make it more 'considerate,' or easier to read and understand. The features should have clear concepts, consistent text structure, references that are easy to locate, and vocabulary that is precise and relates clearly to the subject. . . . A considerate text makes comprehension easier" (Dyck & Pemberton, 2002).*

(Continues)

(Continued)

Passwords: Science Vocabulary Uses . . .	Research Says . . .
Graphic Organizers (Semantic Feature Analysis & Semantic Mapping) (TG, Pre- & Post-reading Activities)	*Hedrick, Harmon, & Linerode (2004, 2000) have analyzed content-area textbooks and have concluded that "textbooks infrequently include visual representations of concepts as a vocabulary instructional strategy."* *"Students with very limited English proficiency show their understanding in a variety of ways. ELL students can demonstrate their knowledge through visual representations" (Crowther, 2006).*
Clear and Explicit Illustrations and Artwork (SB, Reading Passages)	*"Giving an ESL student a nonlinguistic representation will provide a way for them to understand the meaning of the term that is not dependent on an understanding of English" (Marzano & Pickering, 2005).* *"Pictures and other graphic aids provide additional sources of meaning other than the definition of a word" (NSTA, 2006).*
Deep Word Study Activities (Roots, Prefixes, Suffixes, Cognates) (SB/TG)	*Students may find learning English easier if there are similar roots and pre/suffixes between their first language and English. Hansen (2006) suggests exploring cognates in order to aid students in making connections between their first language and English.* *"Teaching a word's facets of meaning moves students beyond a narrow definition of a word" (Beck, McKeown, Kucan, 2002).*
Word Play Activities (TG, Take-Home Activities, Word Cards)	*Researchers (Marzano & Pickering, 2005; NSTA, 2006; Paynter, Bodrova, & Doty, 2005) stress that word play builds strong connection to newly learned vocabulary.* *"Activities using words in games, connecting words, and manipulating words creatively result in excellent student learning" (Beck et al., 2002).*
Association/ Connection Methods: (Personal Connection, Picture Connection, Word Connection) (SB/TG, throughout each lesson, Glossary)	*"When teaching academic vocabulary, students should be active in developing their understanding of words and ways to learn them. This can include semantic mapping and word sorts, and illustrating vocabulary words" (NSTA, 2006).* *"This step is particularly important to ESL students. Whereas they might be constrained in their ability to devise a linguistic description, explanation, or example, they will not be constrained in their ability to create a nonlinguistic representation . . . These representations will most likely reflect the students' native culture, which is exactly the intent. Learning academic terms involves making connections with things familiar to us, and these things commonly arise from experiences native to our culture" (Marzano, 2005).*
Modeling Through Audio (*Passwords* Audio CD)	*"When English language learners can simultaneously hear and read content-related information . . . it helps them decipher the text structures commonly found in textbooks" (Rubinstein-Ávila, 2006).*
Read Alouds (TG)	*"Teacher read-alouds are perhaps the most consistent activity used by classroom teachers that provides frequent, if not daily, opportunities to enhance the literacy of ELLs by integrating effective vocabulary development practices" (Hickman, Pollard-Durodola, & Vaughn, 2004).*
Speaking, Listening, Reading, Writing Experiences (SB/TG, throughout each lesson)	*"Successful word learning is active. Students learn words by using them. Thinking, saying, and writing new words help us make new words our own" (Bromley, 2003).* *García (1999) recommended that teachers use ". . . curriculum materials that are rich in opportunities for speaking, listening, reading, and writing in English."*

References

Alber, S. R., & Foil, C. R. (2002). Fun and effective ways to build your students' vocabulary. *Intervention in School & Clinic, 37.*

Allington, R. L. (2005). The other five "pillars" of effective reading instruction. *Reading Today, 22*(6).

Anderson, T. H., & Armbruster, B. B. (1984). Studying. In P. D. Pearson, R. Barr, M. L. Kamil, & P. Mosenthal (Eds.), *Handbook of reading research* (Vol. 1, pp. 657–679). White Plains, NY: Longman.

Antunez, B. (2002). English language learners and the five essential components of reading comprehension. Accessed February 27, 2006 from http://www.readingrockets.org/articles/341#vocab.

Asher, J. (1969). The total physical response approach to second language learning. *Modern Language Journal, 53,* 3–18.

Association of American Publishers. (Fall 2004). English Language Learners summit proceedings, AAP School Division. Summit on English Language Learners. The Washington Court Hotel, Washington, DC. October 12, 2004. Accessed January 16, 2006 from http://www.publishers.org/SchoolDiv/research/research_03/research_03_Rep_05.htm.

August, D., Carlo, M., Dressler, C., & Snow, C. (2005). The critical role of vocabulary development for English language learners. *Learning Disabilities Research & Practice, 20*(1), 50–57.

Baumann, J. F., Kame'enui, E. J., & Ash, G. E. (2003). Research on vocabulary instruction: Voltaire redux. In J. Flood, D. Lapp, J. R. Squire, & J. M. Jensen (Eds.), *Handbook of research on the teaching of the English language arts* (2nd ed., pp. 752–785). Mahwah, NJ: Erlbaum.

Beck, I., & McKeown, M. (2001). Text talk: Capturing the benefits of read-aloud experiences for young children. *Reading Teacher, 55*(1), 10–20.

Beck, I. L., McKeown, M. G., & Kucan, L. (2002). *Bringing words to life: Robust vocabulary instruction.* New York: Guilford Press.

Bromley, K. (2003, April). Vocabulary S-t-r-e-t-c-h-e-r-s, *Instructor, 112*(7).

Crowther, D. T. (Ed.). (2006). *Science for English-language Learners: K–12 Classroom Strategies.* Arlington, VA: NSTA Press.

Dobb, F. (2004). *Essential elements of science instruction for English learners,* 2nd ed. Los Angeles, CA: California Science Project.

Drucker, M. J. (2003). What reading teachers should know about ESL learners: Good teaching is teaching for all. *The Reading Teacher, 57*(1).

Dyck, N., & Pemberton, J. B. (2002). A model for making decisions about text adaptations. *Intervention in School & Clinic, 38*(1).

Fathman, A. K., & Crowther, D. T. (Eds.). (2006). *Science for English language learners: K–12 classroom strategies.* Arlington, VA: NSTA Press.

García, E. (1999). *Student cultural diversity: Understanding and meeting the challenge* (2nd ed.). Boston: Houghton Mifflin.

Graves, M. F., & Watts-Taffe, S. M. (2002). The place of word consciousness in a research-based vocabulary program in *What Research has to say about reading instruction.* Newark, DE: International Reading Association.

Hansen, L. (2006). Strategies for ELL success: Simple strategies to incorporate into inquiry science for English language learners. *Science and Children,* 23–25.

Hedrick, W. B., Harmon, J. M., & Linerode, P. M. (2004). Teachers' beliefs and practices of vocabulary instruction with social studies textbooks in Grades 4–8. *Reading Horizons, 45*(2), 103–125.

Hedrick, W. B., Harmon, J. M., & Linerode, P. M. (2000). Content analysis of vocabulary instruction in social studies textbooks for grades 4–8. *Elementary School Journal, 100*(3), 253–271.

Henderson, A. T., & Mapp, K. L. (2002). *A new wave of evidence: The impact of school, family, and community connections on student achievement. Annual Synthesis 2002.* National Center for Family & Community Connections with Schools. Austin: Southwest Educational Development Laboratory.

Hickman, P., Pollard-Durodola, S., & Vaughn, S. (2004). Storybook reading: Improving vocabulary and comprehension for English-language learners. *Reading Teacher, 57*(8), 720–730.

Jesness, J. (2004). *Teaching English language learners K–12: A quick-start guide for the new teacher.* Thousand Oaks, CA: Corwin Press.

Marzano, R. J., & Pickering, D. J. (2005). *Building Academic Vocabulary: Teacher's manual.* Alexandria, VA: ASCD.

McCarthey, S. J. (2000). Home-school connections: A review of the literature. *Journal of Educational Research, 93*(3), 145–154.

National Reading Panel. (2000). *Report of the national reading panel: Teaching children to read.* Washington, DC: National Institute of Child Health and Human Development.

National Research Council. (2006). Multiple origins, uncertain destinies: Hispanics and the American future. Panel on Hispanics in the United States. M. Tienda and F. Mitchell, eds. Committee on Population, Division of Behavioral and Social Sciences and Education. Washington, DC: The National Academies Press.

Paynter, D. E., Bodrova, E., & Doty, J. K. (2005). *For the love of words: Vocabulary instruction that works, grades K–6.* San Francisco: Jossey-Bass.

Richek, M. A. (2005, February). Words are wonderful: Interactive, time-efficient strategies to teach meaning vocabulary. *Reading Teacher, 58*(5), 414–423.

Rolón, C. A. (2002/2003). Educating Latino students. *Educational Leadership, 60*(4), 40–3.

Rubinstein-Ávila, E. (2006). Connecting With Latino Learners. *Educational Leadership, 63*(5), 38–43.

Slavin, R. E., & Cheung, A. (2005). Synthesis of research on language of reading instruction for English language learners. *Review of Educational Research Summer, 75*(2), 247–284.

Spellings, M. (2006). Secretary Spellings announces national math and science summit for girls and discusses American competitiveness. Accessed March 1, 2006 at http://www.ed.gov/news/pressreleases/2006/02/02282006.html.

Tomlinson, C. A. (2004, April). Differentiation in diverse settings. *School Administrator, 61*(7).

U. S. Department of Education. (2004). *Parental involvement: Title One, Part A Non-regulatory guidance.* Washington, DC: No Child Left Behind.

U. S. Department of Education. (2006). Strengthening Education: Meeting the Challenge of a Changing World. Accessed on February 15, 2006 at http://www.ed.gov/about/inits/ed/competitiveness/challenge.html.

Zelasko, N., & Antunez, B. (2000). *If your child learns in two languages: A parent's guide for improving educational opportunities for children acquiring English as a second language.* National Clearinghouse of Bilingual Education: The George Washington University: Graduate School of Education and Human Development. Washington, DC.

Zwiers, J. (2004/2005). The third language of academic English. *Educational Leadership, 62*(4), 60–63.

LESSON 1

Earth's Structure

(Student Book pages 4–9)

Lesson Summary Earth is divided by mineral composition into the crust, mantle, and core. The crust is continental crust on land and oceanic crust under the oceans. The crust includes the topsoil, the subsoil, and the underlying bedrock. Below the crust, the mantle has a stiff top, soft middle, and hard lower mantle. The core consists of the outer core of molten nickel and iron, and the solid inner core of the same metals. The inner core remains solid because of the extreme pressure.

TARGET VOCABULARY

continental crust the part of Earth's crust that makes up the land, or continents

oceanic crust the part of Earth's crust that is under the oceans

mantle the layer of Earth below the crust

outer core the layer of molten iron and nickel just below the mantle

molten so hot it becomes liquid

inner core the layer of solid metal at the very center of Earth

topsoil the upper layer of soil

humus decayed plant and animal matter

subsoil the layer of soil below the topsoil

bedrock the solid layer of crust that seems firmly attached to Earth

COGNATES

Spanish-speaking students may find a discussion of the similarities and differences between English and Spanish cognates helpful.

English	Spanish
continental crust	corteza continental
oceanic crust	corteza oceanica
mantle	manto
humus	humus
subsoil	subsuelo

VOCABULARY STRATEGY: Compound Words

Point out that the word *bedrock* combines the words *bed* and *rock*. Have students define the words *bed* and *rock* separately, and then challenge them to explain how the parts relate to the meaning of the compound word. (A *bed* is the platform upon which something or someone rests; *rock* is what this "bed" is made of.) Ask students to list other compounds formed with *bed* or *rock* (bedroom, bedroll, bedtime, rockbound, rockslide, rocklike, etc.).

BEFORE READING

Activate Prior Knowledge

Tell students that Earth's surface has many features, such as mountains and oceans. Have students suggest other features. Ask student volunteers what they think lies underneath each feature they have suggested. Write this incomplete sentence on the board, "I think that ___ lies underneath ___ ." Then have students take turns completing the sentence. Accept all reasonable answers. Tell students that in this lesson they will discover if their answers are correct.

Introduce Target Vocabulary

Tell students they are about to read a selection about Earth's structure. Write the target vocabulary words on the board. Model the pronunciation of each word and have student volunteers repeat the word. Discuss the meaning of each word and, if necessary, write the definition next to the word.

Present Graphic Organizer

Provide each student with a copy of Vocabulary Graphic Organizer: Word Web, Teacher Guide page 76. Have students write *Earth's Structure* in the center circle of the web. As they read the lesson, have students group related target vocabulary words in the outer circles. Have them write a phrase next to each circle that explains why they grouped the words together. Tell them they may add circles, if necessary.

Word and Definition Cards
for Lesson 1 are on pages 99 and 100
of the Teacher Guide.

Earth's Structure

LESSON 1

| continental crust | mantle | molten | topsoil | subsoil |
| oceanic crust | outer core | inner core | humus | bedrock |

Every day, you walk on the surface of Earth. You know what the surface looks like. Have you ever wondered what it is made of and what lies beneath? Read this selection to find out.

Earth's Structure

The Crust and the Mantle

Earth has three main layers that are based on the type of matter they contain. Earth's outer layer is called the crust. The crust is a fairly thin layer of solid rock covered with smaller rocks, and soil, sand, or water. Earth's crust is called the **continental crust** under the land, or continents. The **oceanic crust** lies under the oceans.

Below the crust is the **mantle**, the second main layer. The mantle is a thick layer of rock. The very top part of the mantle forms a cool, stiff shell. Under this shell is a soft layer of mantle. Rocks in this soft layer become so hot that some of them melt. Below the soft layer are the rocks of the lower mantle, which are hard, but still very hot.

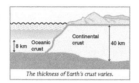

The thickness of Earth's crust varies.

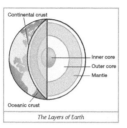

The Layers of Earth

The Core

Beneath the mantle, the third main layer is the core. The core has two parts. The **outer core** is the part closest to the mantle. The outer core is so hot that its metals become liquid. **Molten** iron and nickel make up the outer core. The **inner core**, at the very center of Earth, is even hotter. But the pressure is so strong, the metals remain solid.

Soil

On land, soil makes up much of the surface of Earth. Soil is the part of the crust in which plants can grow. The upper layer of soil is **topsoil**. It contains tiny bits of rock broken up from the solid rock below. It also contains **humus**, which is decayed plant and animal matter. Humus makes the soil rich and dark colored. It provides nutrients that plants need to grow.

Below the topsoil is the **subsoil**, which has bigger pieces of rock. The subsoil contains little humus. Under the subsoil, there are larger broken rocks.

Bedrock

All the pieces of broken rock in the soil layers come from bedrock. **Bedrock** is the solid layer of crust that seems firmly attached to Earth. In most places, bedrock is buried deep under broken rocks, sand, and soil. But in some places, bedrock is at the surface.

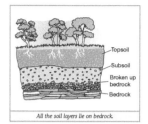

All the soil layers lie on bedrock.

Roads sometimes cut through bedrock.

 My Science Vocabulary
Go to page 94 to list other words you have learned about Earth's structure.

DURING READING

Read the selection aloud to students, stopping at the end of each paragraph or section. Review any words or concepts that students are having trouble with. Remind students that there is a glossary at the back of their book that contains all of the words that appear in boldfaced type in the lesson.

- Discuss the words *topsoil* and *subsoil*. Point out that *topsoil*, a compound word using the word *top*, is, in fact, the layer at the top of the soil. *Subsoil*, on the other hand, uses the prefix *sub-*, meaning "below" or "under." Subsoil is under topsoil.

- Explain to students that the word *molten* is an old-fashioned way of saying "melted." Though the word is not commonly used today in normal speech, it has kept its use as a science term.

- Direct students to the diagram of continental and oceanic crust on page 4. Ask students to explain the difference between continental crust and oceanic crust. (*Continental crust is thicker and lies under the land, or continents. Oceanic crust is thinner and lies under the oceans.*)

- Reinforce the meaning of *humus* by having students examine some rich, sterilized potting soil. They should be able to see some of the organic matter, such as bits of stems and leaves. Explain that this humus makes the soil richer for plants and helps keep it moist.

Have students read the selection again on their own.

AFTER READING

Review Graphic Organizers

Answer any questions students have about the reading selection. Then have students complete or review their graphic organizer and share it with the class.

Summarize

Have students work together to come up with either a written or an oral summary of the lesson. Encourage students to use the target vocabulary words as the basis of their summary. Have students share their summary with the class.

My Science Vocabulary

Encourage students to turn to My Science Vocabulary on page 94 of the student book and use the space provided to add other words about Earth's structure.

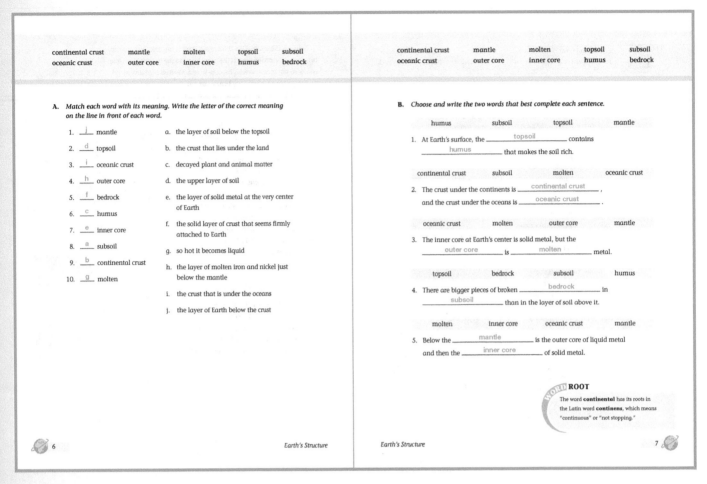

ACTIVITIES A–D

Encourage students to complete as many of the activities as possible. Remind students that they may refer to the Glossary at the back of their book as they complete the activities. Students may work independently, in small groups, or as a class. When students are done, discuss the answers for each activity.

Extensions

These extension ideas allow you to reuse or expand upon the activities. Share them with students who complete the activities before other students, or have students do them for additional practice with the target vocabulary words.

A Divide each target vocabulary word into syllables. Draw a line between each syllable.

B Find smaller words within the target vocabulary words, such as *ocean* in *oceanic,* or *hum* and *us* in *humus.* Put a star next to each smaller word whose meaning relates to the larger word.

WORD ROOT

Point out that *continental* is made up of the word *continent* plus the suffix *-al.* Ask students how the definition of *continens* relates to the meaning of *continent (a large, continuous body of land).*

C Circle all the words that begin with capital letters. Write rules about capitalization based on the words you circled.

D Rewrite each sentence as a question that can be answered "yes" or "no."

continental crust	mantle	molten	topsoil	subsoil
oceanic crust	outer core	inner core	humus	bedrock

C. *Choose the correct vocabulary word to complete each sentence.*

1. The solid _____bedrock_____ is the layer of crust that seems attached to Earth.

2. Earth's deepest layer, the _____inner core_____, is solid metal.

3. When plants and animals decay, they add _____humus_____ to the soil.

4. The larger pieces of rock found in _____subsoil_____ have broken off from the bedrock below.

5. The outer core is so hot that its metals become _____molten_____.

6. The crust found under the Atlantic Ocean is _____oceanic crust_____.

7. The layer of soil that has the most humus is _____topsoil_____.

8. Just below the mantle lies the _____outer core_____ of molten iron and nickel.

9. The crust under the Rocky Mountains is the _____continental crust_____.

10. The layer of Earth between the crust and the core is the _____mantle_____.

---

continental crust	mantle	molten	topsoil	subsoil
oceanic crust	outer core	inner core	humus	bedrock

Students' answers will vary.

D. *Use each pair of words in a sentence.*

1. outer core, molten
   Heat causes metals in the outer core to become molten.

2. topsoil, humus
   The humus in topsoil provides nutrients for growing plants.

3. subsoil, bedrock
   When bedrock breaks apart, some pieces become part of the subsoil.

4. continental crust, oceanic crust
   Earth's crust is called continental crust under the land and oceanic crust under the oceans.

5. mantle, inner core
   The layers of Earth go from crust to mantle to outer core to inner core.

 Write! _____
Write your response to the prompt on a separate sheet of paper. Use as many vocabulary words as you can in your writing.

If you could travel from the core of Earth to the crust, what would you see? Describe how the main layers of Earth change.

Write!

Distribute Writing Graphic Organizer: Main Idea and Details Chart, Teacher Guide page 80. Tell students to write a main idea about the layers of Earth in the Main Idea box. Then have them describe in the Details boxes how the layers are different.

Sample Answer

The three main layers of Earth are the crust, the mantle, and the core. If I could travel from the inside of the Earth, I would begin in the solid, inner core. Then I would pass through a liquid outer core and enter the mantle. The mantle would have a thick layer of rock, then a soft layer of very hot rock, and then rock again. I would pass into the crust, seeing bedrock under the soil. If I came up under an ocean, I would break through oceanic crust. Under land, I would break through continental crust. It might be covered by subsoil with large rock pieces and then topsoil with humus.

TAKE-HOME ACTIVITY

Assign the Take-Home Activity to students for additional practice with the target vocabulary words. The reproducible Take-Home Activity for Lesson 1 is on page 84 of the Teacher Guide.

Earth's Structure

TAKE HOME 1

continental crust	mantle	molten	topsoil	subsoil
oceanic crust	outer core	inner core	humus	bedrock

Use vocabulary words to complete the puzzle.

Earth's Structure

ACROSS

1. the layer of soil under the topsoil
7. the part of Earth's crust under the continents
9. the part of Earth's crust under the oceans
10. the upper layer of soil

DOWN

2. the solid layer of crust that seems firmly attached to Earth
3. the layer of molten metal just below the mantle
4. the layer of Earth below the crust
5. so hot it becomes liquid
6. the layer of solid metal at the very center of Earth
8. decayed plant and animal matter

 Tell someone in your family what you have learned about Earth's structure.

LESSON 2
Earth's Moving Plates

(Student Book pages 10–15)

Lesson Summary The solid, outer layer of Earth is the lithosphere. The lithosphere, which includes the crust and the top part of the mantle, rests on the soft part of the mantle. The lithosphere is divided into plates. According to plate tectonics, convection currents in the soft, mid-mantle layer move the plates slowly by a process called continental drift. At plate boundaries, this movement results in faults, ridges, folded mountains, rift valleys, and seafloor spreading.

TARGET VOCABULARY

lithosphere the solid outer layer of Earth

plate a section of the lithosphere

plate tectonics the model that explains how Earth's moving plates create landforms

convection current the very slow up-and-down movement of soft rock of the mantle

continental drift the movement of Earth's plates

fault a break in Earth's crust

ridge a long row of sharp mountains

folding the bending up of Earth's crust where plates push together

rift a deep underwater valley where Earth's plates are moving apart

seafloor spreading the forming of new oceanic crust at a rift

COGNATES

Spanish-speaking students may find a discussion of the similarities and differences between English and Spanish cognates helpful.

English	Spanish
lithosphere	litosfera
plate	placa
plate tectonics	tectónica de placas
convection current	corriente de convección
continental drift	deriva continental
fault	falla

BEFORE READING

Activate Prior Knowledge

Show students a world map or globe. Point out the shapes of coastlines of continents, such as eastern North and South America and western Africa. Have students describe the coastlines and share ideas about why they look alike. Have each student write the idea they think is best.

Introduce Target Vocabulary

Tell students they are about to read a selection about Earth's moving plates. Write the target vocabulary words on the board. Model the pronunciation of each word and have student volunteers repeat the word. Discuss the meaning of each word and, if necessary, write the definition next to the word.

Present Graphic Organizer

Provide each student with a copy of Vocabulary Graphic Organizer: Venn Diagram, Teacher Guide page 77. Have students title one circle *Plates Spreading Apart* and one *Plates Pushing Together*. As they read the lesson, have students write the target vocabulary words under the title that seems most appropriate. Point out that the overlap of the circles is for words that fit under both titles.

Word and Definition Cards
for Lesson 2 are on pages 101 and 102
of the Teacher Guide.

VOCABULARY STRATEGY: Print Features

Explain to students that material meant to convey information often uses special features to highlight words or phrases. The lessons in this book use boldfaced type for certain words. Ask what the boldfaced type might be for *(to make students notice and pay attention to the word)*. Tell students that in this text, definitions often appear near the boldfaced word. Have them pick out examples of these definitions by underlining them in the text.

Earth's Moving Plates

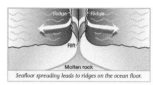

LESSON 2

lithosphere	convection current	ridge	rift
plate	continental drift	folding	seafloor spreading
plate tectonics	fault		

The land you walk on seems solid and still. But did you know that all of it is floating and moving? Read this selection to find out what happens when the land moves.

Earth's Moving Plates

The outer part of Earth is made of solid rock. It consists of Earth's thin crust and the stiff top part of the middle layer, or mantle. This solid, outer layer of Earth is called the **lithosphere**.

The lithosphere is made up of sections. Each section is a **plate**. The plates float on the hot, soft rocks of the middle of the mantle.

The lithosphere floats on the soft rock of the mantle.

The Movement of Earth's Land

Plate tectonics is the model that explains the movement of the lithosphere. The model explains how the plates create landforms, such as mountains and valleys, as they move.

The lithosphere is divided into six large plates and more than a dozen smaller plates.

Continental Drift

Because the plates of the lithosphere are not connected, convection currents can make the plates move. A **convection current** is the very slow up-and-down movement of rock within the soft part of Earth's mantle. This movement is caused by heating and cooling. Convection currents occur because the rock is hotter at the bottom and cooler at the top.

As the convection currents in the mantle move the plates, continents or parts of continents are carried slowly toward or away from one another. The plates move a few centimeters a year. The movement of the plates is called **continental drift**.

Effects of the Moving Plates

Many events occur at the edges of the plates. Two plates can slide past each other along a fault. A **fault** is a break in Earth's crust. When one plate on the edge of a fault slips upward, a ridge forms. A **ridge** is a long row of sharp mountains.

Plates can also push toward each other, causing folding. **Folding** is the bending upward of Earth's crust to make waves, or folds, of mountains. Some of Earth's highest mountains were formed by folding.

Folding pushes up mountains.

Plates can also move apart. When plates move away from each other, a **rift**, or deep valley, forms. In the deep ocean, molten rock wells up from the mantle into the rift. As the molten rock flows up and outward, ridges of new crust form on either side of the rift. This process is called **seafloor spreading**.

Seafloor spreading leads to ridges on the ocean floor.

My Science Vocabulary
Go to page 94 to list other words you have learned about Earth's moving plates.

10   Earth's Moving Plates

Earth's Moving Plates   11

DURING READING

Read the selection aloud to students, stopping at the end of each paragraph or section. Review any words or concepts that students are having trouble with. Remind students that there is a glossary at the back of their book that contains all of the words that appear in boldfaced type in the lesson.

- Tell students that the Greek prefix *litho-* means "stone" and the Greek word *sphaira*, which means "ball," is the root of the English word *sphere*. Ask how the meanings of the prefix and root relate to the word *lithosphere. (The lithosphere is the solid stone ball of Earth's crust.)* Encourage students to add this information to the root words chart on page 99 of their book.

- Have students cut a paper plate in half in a wavy line, move the pieces apart, and fit them together to observe continental drift by plates.

- Tell students that seafloor spreading is similar to what happens when you squeeze a toothpaste tube. The opening is the rift. The toothpaste flowing out to the sides forms ridges.

- Refer students to the diagram of folding on page 11. Have students demonstrate and explain *folding* by pushing on the edges of a sheet of paper.

Have students read the selection again on their own.

AFTER READING

Review Graphic Organizers

Answer any questions students have about the reading selection. Then have students complete or review their graphic organizer and share it with the class.

Summarize

Have students work together to come up with either a written or an oral summary of the lesson. Encourage students to use the target vocabulary words as the basis of their summary. Have students share their summary with the class.

My Science Vocabulary

Encourage students to turn to My Science Vocabulary on page 94 of the student book and use the space provided to add other words about Earth's moving plates.

lithosphere	convection current	ridge	rift
plate	continental drift	folding	seafloor spreading
plate tectonics	fault		

A. Fill in the blanks with the correct vocabulary word.

1. a section of the lithosphere that floats on the hot, soft rocks of the mantle
   p l a t e

2. a long row of sharp mountains
   r i d g e

3. a break in Earth's crust
   f a u l t

4. a deep underwater valley that forms when Earth's plates move apart
   r i f t

5. the model that explains how Earth's plates create landforms as they move
   p l a t e   t e c t o n i c s

6. the solid outer part of Earth that consists of the crust and the top part of the mantle
   l i t h o s p h e r e

7. the up-and-down movement of soft rock within Earth's mantle
   c o n v e c t i o n   c u r r e n t

8. the bending upward of Earth's crust to form mountains
   f o l d i n g

9. the process by which molten rock flows up and outward through a rift to form ridges of new crust on the ocean floor
   s e a f l o o r   s p r e a d i n g

10. the slow movement of Earth's plates that carries continents or parts of continents toward or away from one another
    c o n t i n e n t a l   d r i f t

lithosphere	convection current	ridge	rift
plate	continental drift	folding	seafloor spreading
plate tectonics	fault		

B. Circle the word that makes sense in each sentence. Then write the word.

1. The (lithosphere, convection current) is the rocky outer part of Earth.
   lithosphere

2. At a rift under the ocean, (folding, seafloor spreading) builds new crust. seafloor spreading

3. Plates can slide past one another along a (fault, lithosphere).
   fault

4. In the mantle, a (fault, convection current) occurs because the soft rock is hotter at the bottom and cooler at the top. convection current

5. The model of (rift, plate tectonics) explains the way landforms are created as the lithosphere moves. plate tectonics

6. When plates move apart, a (ridge, plate) of new crust forms on either side of the rift. ridge

7. Each section of the lithosphere is called a (ridge, plate).
   plate

8. Two plates pushing toward each other may cause (folding, seafloor spreading). folding

9. Under the ocean where new crust is forming, plates have moved apart at a (continental drift, rift). rift

10. Convection currents in the mantle cause the slow movement called (lithosphere, continental drift). continental drift

WORD ROOT

The word **tectonics** comes from the Greek root **tekton**, which means "builder."

ACTIVITIES A–D

Encourage students to complete as many of the activities as possible. Remind students that they may refer to the Glossary at the back of their book as they complete the activities. Students may work independently, in small groups, or as a class. When students are done, discuss the answers for each activity.

Extensions

These extension ideas allow you to reuse or expand upon the activities. Share them with students who complete the activities before other students, or have students do them for additional practice with the target vocabulary words.

A Add an adjective before any noun in each target vocabulary word's definition.

B Look up each target vocabulary word in a dictionary. If the vocabulary word is made up of two words, look up each word separately. Compare the definition(s) to those in the Glossary. If a definition is not exactly the same, tell how the definition is similar and how it is different.

WORD ROOT

Ask students how the meaning "builder" relates to the target vocabulary word *plate tectonics*. (*Plate tectonics is the model that relates how the lithosphere is built of plates, and how these plates build landforms.*)

C Have each student rewrite one of the pairs of sentences as a single sentence.

D Challenge students to circle the verb or verb phrase in each of the sentences.

lithosphere convection current ridge rift
plate continental drift folding seafloor spreading
plate tectonics fault

C. *Write the vocabulary word that best completes each pair of sentences.*

1. A break in the crust is a ____fault____.
   Plates can slide past each other or lift upward at a ____fault____.

2. When plates push toward each other, ____folding____ can occur.
   The process of ____folding____ results in waves of mountains.

3. A ____convection current____ can make Earth's plates move.
   Heating and cooling cause a ____convection current____ in the mantle.

4. The movement of the lithosphere is explained by ____plate tectonics____.
   The model of ____plate tectonics____ explains how landforms are created.

5. A deep ____rift____ can be found between ridges in the ocean.
   New crust forms at a ____rift____.

6. The movement of plates is ____continental drift____.
   Plates are moved a few centimeters a year by ____continental drift____.

7. A long row of sharp mountains is a ____ridge____.
   A ____ridge____ may form at a fault on land or at a rift in the sea.

8. Under the ocean at a rift, or deep valley, ____seafloor spreading____ is occurring.
   The process of ____seafloor spreading____ results in new crust on the ocean floor.

9. Earth's solid outer layer is the ____lithosphere____.
   The crust and top part of the mantle make up the ____lithosphere____.

10. Each section of the lithosphere that floats on the soft mantle is a ____plate____.
    When one ____plate____ pushes toward another, folds of mountains may form.

14   *Earth's Moving Plates*

---

lithosphere convection current ridge rift
plate continental drift folding seafloor spreading
plate tectonics fault

Students' answers will vary.

D. *Use each word in a sentence that shows you understand the meaning of the word.*

1. plate ___A plate is a section of the lithosphere.___

2. folding ___Folding pushes up high mountains.___

3. convection current ___A convection current occurs because soft rock in the mantle is hotter at the bottom and cooler at the top.___

4. plate tectonics ___The model of plate tectonics explains how mountains and valleys form.___

5. seafloor spreading ___New crust under the ocean is made by seafloor spreading.___

6. ridge ___A ridge may appear along a fault or a rift.___

7. rift ___When plates move apart, a rift forms.___

8. lithosphere ___The solid outer layer of Earth is the lithosphere.___

9. continental drift ___The movement of plates is continental drift.___

10. fault ___Two plates can slide past one another at a fault.___

Write! ___

Write your response to the prompt on a separate sheet of paper. Use as many vocabulary words as you can in your writing.

Suppose that you could stand above Earth for millions of years and see its plates moving. What would you notice about the changing surface of Earth?

Earth's Moving Plates   15

Write!

Distribute Writing Graphic Organizer: Idea Wheel, Teacher Guide page 81. Tell students to write *Earth's Changing Surface* in the center of the wheel. Then on the spokes of the wheel, they should write changes they would notice. Tell students they may add spokes to the wheel, if necessary.

Sample Answer

 At first, I see all the plates of the lithosphere together. Then plate tectonics takes over. Convection currents move the plates around. A faults forms. As the plates slide past each other, a ridge is pushed up. Two plates move slowly apart, showing continental drift. Two other plates push against each other to cause folding. Under the ocean, a rift valley forms, and ridges are created with new crust by seafloor spreading.

TAKE-HOME ACTIVITY

Assign the Take-Home Activity to students for additional practice with the target vocabulary words. The reproducible Take-Home Activity for Lesson 2 is on page 85 of the Teacher Guide.

TAKE HOME 2

lithosphere convection current ridge rift
plate continental drift folding seafloor spreading
plate tectonics fault

Use vocabulary words to complete the puzzle.

Earth's Moving Plates

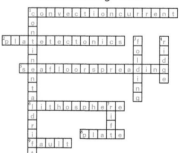

ACROSS

1 the slow up-and-down movement of rock in the soft part of Earth's mantle

2 the model that explains the movement of Earth's plates

5 the process of oceanic plates moving apart at a rift

6 the solid outer part of Earth

8 one section of lithosphere

9 a break in Earth's crust

DOWN

1 the movement of Earth's plates toward and away from each other

3 the bending up of Earth's crust where plates push together

4 a long row of sharp mountains

7 a deep underwater valley where Earth's plates move apart

 Tell someone in your family what you have learned about Earth's moving plates.

©Curriculum Associates, LLC *Passwords: Science Vocabulary, Earth Science, Lesson 2* 85

Earth's Moving Plates   23

LESSON 3

Earthquakes

(Student Book pages 16–21)

TARGET VOCABULARY

fault line the line of a fault on Earth's surface

shock waves strong waves of energy

focus the point underground where an earthquake begins

seismic waves shock waves of an earthquake

epicenter the point on Earth's surface right above the focus

seismograph a tool that records the time and strength of earthquakes

magnitude the size and strength of an earthquake

Richter scale one scale for measuring earthquake magnitude

tremor a small earthquake

aftershock a smaller earthquake that follows a large earthquake

COGNATES

Spanish-speaking students may find a discussion of the similarities and differences between English and Spanish cognates helpful.

English	Spanish
fault	falla
line	línea
focus	foco
seismic waves	ondas sísmicas
epicenter	epicentro
seismograph	sismógrafo
magnitude	magnitud
Richter scale	escala de Richter
tremor	temblor

VOCABULARY STRATEGY: Context Clues

Tell students that one way to understand new words is to use clues that the writer has provided. These types of clues are called context clues. One type of context clue is the definition of a word. Have students find the context clue at the start of the lesson that defines *earthquake*. (*An earthquake is a sudden movement of Earth's crust.*) Point out that words such as *is* and *means* may signal that the writer is giving a definition. Have students find and read aloud one or more additional examples of context clues that give the definition of a boldfaced word in the selection.

Lesson Summary An earthquake, a sudden movement of Earth's crust, usually occurs at a fault. An earthquake begins underground at its focus. Shock waves, or seismic waves, move outward from the focus, reaching the epicenter, the surface above the focus. Scientists use a seismograph to record the strength of an earthquake and may use the Richter scale to report the magnitude. On this scale, a tremor has the magnitude 1 or 2. Earthquakes over 6 generally cause much damage.

BEFORE READING

Activate Prior Knowledge

Have students volunteer all the information they think they know about earthquakes. Make a list on the board of these "earthquake facts." Have students add to or revise the list as they read the lesson.

Introduce Target Vocabulary

Tell students they are about to read a selection about earthquakes. Write the target vocabulary words on the board. Model the pronunciation of each word and have student volunteers repeat the word. Discuss the meaning of each word and, if necessary, write the definition next to the word.

Present Graphic Organizer

Provide each student with a copy of Vocabulary Graphic Organizer: Four Square, Teacher Guide page 78. Assign each student one target vocabulary word to write in the center. Have students label the boxes: *What Does It Mean? What Is It? Where or How Is It Found? Why Is It Important?* As students read the lesson, have them answer the question in each box.

Word and Definition Cards
for Lesson 3 are on pages 103 and 104
of the Teacher Guide.

Earthquakes

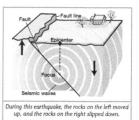
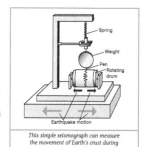
DURING READING

Read the selection aloud to students, stopping at the end of each paragraph or section. Review any words or concepts that students are having trouble with. Remind students that there is a glossary at the back of their book that contains all of the words that appear in boldfaced type in the lesson.

- Have students copy an earthquake drawing, such as the diagram on page 17 of their book, or find one on the Internet. Have them use the labels *fault line, focus, epicenter, shock waves/seismic waves* on their diagram.

- Point out that *epi-* means "over or above." Ask students to explain how that meaning relates to the word *epicenter (above the focus)*. Encourage students to add this information to the prefix chart on page 100 of their book.

- Point out the compound *aftershock*. Ask what its parts suggest *(a shock, or shaking, after the first shock)*.

- Tell students that in Latin, *magnus* means "great." Have them tell how the meaning relates to the word *magnitude (the greatness, or largeness, of the earthquake)*.

Have students read the selection again on their own.

AFTER READING

Review Graphic Organizers

Answer any questions students have about the reading selection. Then have students complete or review their graphic organizer and share it with the class.

Summarize

Have students work together to come up with either a written or an oral summary of the lesson. Encourage students to use the target vocabulary words as the basis of their summary. Have students share their summary with the class.

My Science Vocabulary

Encourage students to turn to My Science Vocabulary on page 94 of the student book and use the space provided to add other words about earthquakes.

Earthquakes   25

Worksheet page 18:

fault line   focus   epicenter   magnitude   tremor
shock waves   seismic waves   seismograph   Richter scale   aftershock

A. Match each word with its meaning. Write the letter of the correct meaning on the line in front of each word.

1. _b_ focus
2. _j_ seismograph
3. _h_ Richter scale
4. _g_ aftershock
5. _d_ tremor
6. _a_ fault line
7. _e_ epicenter
8. _c_ seismic waves
9. _i_ magnitude
10. _f_ shock waves

a. the line where a fault shows on Earth's surface

b. where an earthquake begins

c. shock waves produced by an earthquake

d. a small shaking of Earth's crust

e. the point on Earth's surface above the focus

f. strong energy waves, such as seismic waves

g. a smaller earthquake after a large earthquake

h. a scale that measures an earthquake's magnitude

i. the strength of an earthquake

j. a tool that measures and records seismic waves

18   *Earthquakes*

Worksheet page 19:

fault line   focus   epicenter   magnitude   tremor
shock waves   seismic waves   seismograph   Richter scale   aftershock

B. Circle the word that makes sense in each sentence. Then write the word.

1. The point on Earth's surface right above the focus is the (epicenter, seismograph). _____ epicenter

2. After the first earthquake, an (aftershock, epicenter) may occur. _____ aftershock

3. Scientists use the (focus, Richter scale) to measure an earthquake's magnitude. _____ Richter scale

4. Shock waves that move out from the focus of an earthquake are known as (seismograph, seismic waves). _____ seismic waves

5. An earthquake that is hardly felt is a (magnitude, tremor). _____ tremor

6. An earthquake begins at the (fault line, focus). _____ focus

7. When rocks along a fault suddenly move or break, (shock waves, focus) are produced. _____ shock waves

8. The tool used to measure and record seismic waves is a (epicenter, seismograph). _____ seismograph

9. The line of a fault on Earth's surface is the (focus, fault line). _____ fault line

10. The amount of energy released by an earthquake is its (tremor, magnitude). _____ magnitude

WORD ROOT
The word **seismic** is from the Greek word **seismos**, which means "trembling Earth."

Earthquakes   19

ACTIVITIES A–D

Encourage students to complete as many of the activities as possible. Remind students that they may refer to the Glossary at the back of their book as they complete the activities. Students may work independently, in small groups, or as a class. When students are done, discuss the answers for each activity.

Extensions

These extension ideas allow you to reuse or expand upon the activities. Share them with students who complete the activities before other students, or have students do them for additional practice with the target vocabulary words.

A Put the target vocabulary words in alphabetical order.

B Make all the target vocabulary words that are singular nouns into plural nouns (except *Richter scale*) and all that are plural nouns into singular nouns. Explain why *Richter scale* cannot be changed. (Note: The plural of *focus* can be *focuses* or *foci*.)

WORD ROOT

Ask students how *seismos* relates to the meaning of *seismic waves*. (*They are waves caused by the trembling of Earth's crust.*) Tell students that *graph* means "something that writes or records." Have them explain *seismograph* (*the tool records seismic wave height*). Have students list other words that include *graph*, such as *telegraph* and *graphic*.

C Group the target vocabulary words into the categories: *Parts of an Earthquake, Measuring Earthquakes,* and *Earthquake Energy.* Justify the choices of words for each category.

D Underline the complete subject(s) and circle the complete predicate(s) in each of the sentences.

fault line   focus   epicenter   magnitude   tremor
shock waves   seismic waves   seismograph   Richter scale   aftershock

C. *Choose the correct vocabulary word to complete each sentence.*

1. Seismic waves reach Earth's surface at the _____epicenter_____ .

2. Scientists use the term _____seismic waves_____ to name shock waves from an earthquake.

3. An earthquake begins underground at the _____focus_____ .

4. A very strong earthquake may have a magnitude of 9 on the _____Richter scale_____ .

5. A fault can be seen on Earth's surface at the _____fault line_____ .

6. After a large earthquake, an _____aftershock_____ can cause more damage.

7. The strength of an earthquake is its _____magnitude_____ .

8. Scientists use a _____seismograph_____ to measure and record seismic waves.

9. A sudden movement of rocks along a fault causes _____shock waves_____ , or seismic waves.

10. The magnitude of a _____tremor_____ is about 1 to 2 on the Richter scale.

20   *Earthquakes*

---

fault line   focus   epicenter   magnitude   tremor
shock waves   seismic waves   seismograph   Richter scale   aftershock

Students' answers will vary.

D. *Use each pair of words in a sentence.*

1. focus, epicenter
Seismic waves move away from the focus below ground to the epicenter on the surface.

2. magnitude, aftershock
An earthquake of high magnitude can damage buildings, but even more damage can occur in an aftershock.

3. fault line, tremor
People standing near a fault line may feel a tremor.

4. shock waves, seismic waves
Seismic waves are the shock waves of an earthquake.

5. Richter scale, seismograph
Scientists take information from a seismograph and report it, using the Richter scale.

Write!
Write your response to the prompt on a separate sheet of paper. Use as many vocabulary words as you can in your writing.

Suppose you could follow an earthquake from start to finish. What events would be happening at the source and in the area affected by the earthquake?

Earthquakes   21

Write!

Distribute Writing Graphic Organizer: Sequence Chart, Teacher Guide page 83. Tell students to write in the first box of the chart the events that happen at the start of an earthquake. In the following boxes, they should write in order other events they would experience.

Sample Answer

At the start of an earthquake, rocks slide past each other on the fault line. Earth's crust suddenly shifts under the surface. Shock waves, or seismic waves, move out from the focus.

At the epicenter, an earthquake of 5 on the Richter scale shakes buildings. The magnitude is measured on a nearby seismograph. Then the shaking stops. Within a few minutes, people feel an aftershock. Luckily, it is just a tremor.

TAKE-HOME ACTIVITY

Assign the Take-Home Activity to students for additional practice with the target vocabulary words. The reproducible Take-Home Activity for Lesson 3 is on page 86 of the Teacher Guide.

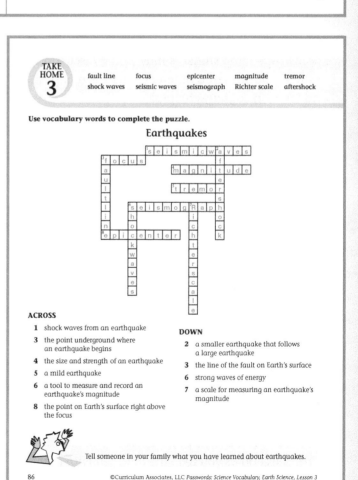

TAKE HOME 3

fault line   focus   epicenter   magnitude   tremor
shock waves   seismic waves   seismograph   Richter scale   aftershock

Use vocabulary words to complete the puzzle.

Earthquakes

ACROSS

1 shock waves from an earthquake
3 the point underground where an earthquake begins
4 the size and strength of an earthquake
5 a mild earthquake
6 a tool to measure and record an earthquake's magnitude
8 the point on Earth's surface right above the focus

DOWN

2 a smaller earthquake that follows a large earthquake
3 the line of the fault on Earth's surface
6 strong waves of energy
7 a scale for measuring an earthquake's magnitude

Tell someone in your family what you have learned about earthquakes.

86   ©Curriculum Associates, LLC *Passwords: Science Vocabulary, Earth Science, Lesson 3*

LESSON 4

Volcanoes

(Student Book pages 22–27)

TARGET VOCABULARY

magma molten rock below Earth's surface

vent a volcano's opening at the surface

lava magma that reaches Earth's surface

volcanic eruption the releasing of magma, gases, or ash from a volcano

fissure a long crack in Earth's crust

cone a volcanic mountain that has a steep top, sloping sides, and a round base

crater a round hole at the top of a volcanic cone

active volcano a volcano that has erupted within the past 10,000 years

dormant volcano a volcano that has not erupted recently

extinct volcano a volcano that hasn't erupted for 10,000 years

COGNATES

Spanish-speaking students may find a discussion of the similarities and differences between English and Spanish cognates helpful.

English	Spanish
magma	magma
lava	lava
volcanic	volcánico
eruption	erupción
fissure	fisura
cone	cono
crater	cráter
active	activo
volcano	volcán
extinct	extinto

VOCABULARY STRATEGY: Context Clues

Context clues are words in a selection that help explain unfamiliar words. One type of context clue includes familiar words to rename an unfamiliar term. These words may be synonyms or synonym phrases. Have students pay attention to the word *vent* in the selection as you read the third sentence of the first paragraph aloud. Ask what word tells what a

Lesson Summary A volcano is an opening in Earth's crust through which magma, volcanic rock, ash, and gases erupt. Magma flows from a chamber deep inside Earth through pipes to vents at the surface. Volcanic eruptions range from a fairly gentle flow through a fissure to an explosive eruption. Some volcanoes form steep-sided cones. A crater may form at the top of the cone. Scientists group volcanoes as active, dormant, or extinct.

BEFORE READING

Activate Prior Knowledge

Have students each draw a sketch of what the word *volcano* suggests to them and give their sketch a name. Post the sketches on the board to review during the lesson.

Introduce Target Vocabulary

Tell students they are about to read a selection about volcanoes. Write the target vocabulary words on the board. Model the pronunciation of each word and have student volunteers repeat the word. Discuss the meaning of each word and, if necessary, write the definition next to the word.

Present Graphic Organizer

Provide each student with a copy of Vocabulary Graphic Organizer: Word Web, Teacher Guide page 76. In the center circle of the web, have half of the students write *Parts and Events of Volcanoes* and the other half *Types of Volcanoes*. Have them add related target vocabulary words to the outer circles as they read the lesson.

Word and Definition Cards
for Lesson 4 are on pages 105 and 106
of the Teacher Guide.

vent is *(opening)*. Explain that words such as *or, known as, also called, such as,* and *like* can signal this type of context clue. Have students find a boldfaced word that gives the meaning clue first and then presents the boldfaced word. (Paragraph 6: *At the top of the cone, a bowl-shaped hole, or* **crater***, may form.*)

Volcanoes

magma   lava   fissure   crater   dormant volcano
vent   volcanic eruption   cone   active volcano   extinct volcano

You may have read about volcanoes erupting or have seen pictures of volcanoes smoking or glowing red-hot. What do you think causes volcanoes? Read this selection to see if you are right.

Volcanoes

The Making of a Volcano

A volcano is an opening in Earth's crust where hot liquid rock and gases rise to the surface. The molten rock is called **magma**. The magma comes from a deep pool, or chamber, inside Earth. The magma then moves through a pipe inside the volcano to a **vent**, or opening at Earth's surface.

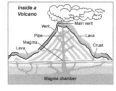

Inside a Volcano

When the magma reaches the surface, it is called **lava**. Lava can flow like a river over the ground. As it cools, lava hardens into volcanic rock.

Volcanic Eruptions

A **volcanic eruption** occurs when molten rock, gas, or ash comes out of a volcano. Most people think of an eruption as a great explosion. But some eruptions are less violent. In some places, magma flows out gently through a fissure. A **fissure** is a long crack in Earth's crust. In other eruptions, thin magma moves gently up through the vent of a volcano.

Fissure at Volcano National Park, Hawaii

Explosive Eruptions

If magma is thick, the vent of a volcano can become blocked. When magma pushing upward through the pipe finally breaks the block, a huge explosion occurs. The volcano throws out lumps of thick lava that become solid as they move through the air. Along with the lava, gases rush out of the vents. Solid rocks that made up the volcano's sides may be hurled into the air too. The volcano also blasts out powdery rock, known as ash.

A volcano that erupts many times may form a cone. A **cone** is a volcanic mountain that has a steep top, sloping sides, and a round base. At the top of the cone, a bowl-shaped hole, or **crater**, may form.

An Erupting Volcano

Stages of a Volcano's Life

Scientists group volcanoes by when they erupted. An **active volcano** is erupting now or has erupted within the past 10,000 years. A **dormant volcano** has not erupted recently. But scientists believe a dormant volcano may still erupt. An **extinct volcano** is unlikely to erupt again. But an extinct volcano can shock people by erupting suddenly.

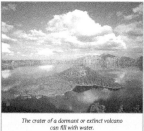

The crater of a dormant or extinct volcano can fill with water.

My Science Vocabulary

Go to page 95 to list other words you have learned about volcanoes.

DURING READING

Read the selection aloud to students, stopping at the end of each paragraph or section. Review any words or concepts that students are having trouble with. Remind students that there is a glossary at the back of their book that contains all of the words that appear in boldfaced type in the lesson.

- Refer students to the diagram of the volcano on page 22. Have a volunteer describe how the magma moves from the magma chamber to the crust while other students trace a path with a finger.

- Draw a horizontal line on the board and label it *Earth's Crust*. Have students come to the board and write *magma, lava,* and *vent* where they would be found during a violent volcanic eruption.

- Have students explain or look up how the words *active, dormant,* and *extinct* are normally used and how they give meaning to the volcano types (active—*"moving, alive"*; dormant—*"sleeping but can wake up"*; extinct—*"died out"*).

Have students read the selection again on their own.

AFTER READING

Review Graphic Organizers

Answer any questions students have about the reading selection. Then have students complete or review their graphic organizer and share it with the class.

Summarize

Have students work together to come up with either a written or an oral summary of the lesson. Encourage students to use the target vocabulary words as the basis of their summary. Have students share their summary with the class.

My Science Vocabulary

Encourage students to turn to My Science Vocabulary on page 95 of the student book and use the space provided to add other words about volcanoes.

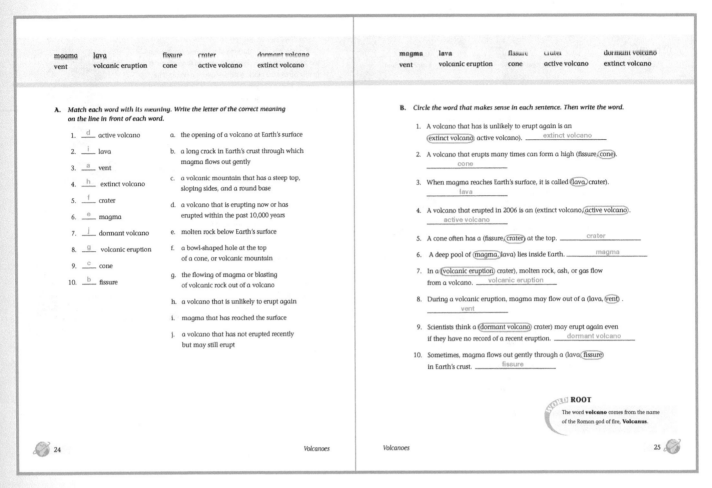

A. Match each word with its meaning. Write the letter of the correct meaning on the line in front of each word.

1. __d__ active volcano
2. __i__ lava
3. __a__ vent
4. __h__ extinct volcano
5. __f__ crater
6. __e__ magma
7. __j__ dormant volcano
8. __g__ volcanic eruption
9. __c__ cone
10. __b__ fissure

a. the opening of a volcano at Earth's surface

b. a long crack in Earth's crust through which magma flows out gently

c. a volcanic mountain that has a steep top, sloping sides, and a round base

d. a volcano that is erupting now or has erupted within the past 10,000 years

e. molten rock below Earth's surface

f. a bowl-shaped hole at the top of a cone, or volcanic mountain

g. the flowing of magma or blasting of volcanic rock out of a volcano

h. a volcano that is unlikely to erupt again

i. magma that has reached the surface

j. a volcano that has not erupted recently but may still erupt

B. Circle the word that makes sense in each sentence. Then write the word.

1. A volcano that has is unlikely to erupt again is an (extinct volcano, active volcano). ____extinct volcano____

2. A volcano that erupts many times can form a high (fissure, cone). ____cone____

3. When magma reaches Earth's surface, it is called (lava, crater). ____lava____

4. A volcano that erupted in 2006 is an (extinct volcano, active volcano). ____active volcano____

5. A cone often has a (fissure, crater) at the top. ____crater____

6. A deep pool of (magma, lava) lies inside Earth. ____magma____

7. In a (volcanic eruption, crater), molten rock, ash, or gas flow from a volcano. ____volcanic eruption____

8. During a volcanic eruption, magma may flow out of a (lava, vent). ____vent____

9. Scientists think a (dormant volcano, crater) may erupt again even if they have no record of a recent eruption. ____dormant volcano____

10. Sometimes, magma flows out gently through a (lava, fissure) in Earth's crust. ____fissure____

ROOT

The word **volcano** comes from the name of the Roman god of fire, **Volcanus**.

ACTIVITIES A–D

Encourage students to complete as many of the activities as possible. Remind students that they may refer to the Glossary at the back of their book as they complete the activities. Students may work independently, in small groups, or as a class. When students are done, discuss the answers for each activity.

Extensions

These extension ideas allow you to reuse or expand upon the activities. Share them with students who complete the activities before other students, or have students do them for additional practice with the target vocabulary words.

A Use books or the Internet to find pictures that illustrate the target vocabulary words.

B Circle all the nouns in the sentences. Underline the verbs.

WORD ROOT

Explain that the Roman god Volcanus, also known as Vulcan, worked as a blacksmith forging tools of destruction. Have students explain how this detail relates to the word *volcano*. (*A volcano is hot like a blacksmith's forge, has melted rock, and can be destructive.*)

C Find one word in each sentence that can be replaced with a synonym or a synonym phrase. Write the new sentence with the replaced word or phrase.

D Write a question to which one of the sentences would be the correct answer.

Worksheet (left page, p. 26)

magma   lava   fissure   crater   dormant volcano
vent   volcanic eruption   cone   active volcano   extinct volcano

C. *Choose the correct vocabulary word to complete each sentence.*

1. When it reaches the surface, magma is called ____lava____ .

2. A long crack through which magma flows out gently is a ____fissure____ .

3. Magma moves through a pipe inside a volcano to a ____vent____ .

4. Mount St. Helens erupted in 1980, so it is called an ____active volcano____ .

5. Volcanic rock may build up and form a ____cone____ with a steep top, sloping sides, and a round base.

6. If a volcano is unlikely to erupt again, it is called an ____extinct volcano____ .

7. When molten rock begins to flow out of a volcano, a ____volcanic eruption____ has begun.

8. The molten rock that moves up a volcano toward the surface is called ____magma____ .

9. If a volcano has not erupted recently but still seems as if it could erupt, it is called a ____dormant volcano____ .

10. A volcanic cone often has a bowl-shaped hole, or ____crater____ , at the top.

 26   *Volcanoes*

Worksheet (right page, p. 27)

magma   lava   fissure   crater   dormant volcano
vent   volcanic eruption   cone   active volcano   extinct volcano

Students' answers will vary.

D. *Use each word in a sentence that shows you understand the meaning of the word.*

1. volcanic eruption ___Most people think of a volcanic eruption as a huge explosion.___

2. fissure ___In a gentle volcanic eruption, magma can flow out through a fissure.___

3. lava ___Lava can flow like a river over the ground.___

4. vent ___Magma flows onto Earth's surface through a vent.___

5. cone ___A cone is a volcanic mountain shaped like a cone.___

6. active volcano ___If a volcano is erupting, you know it's an active volcano.___

7. magma ___The molten rock called magma moves up pipes inside volcanoes.___

8. extinct volcano ___An extinct volcano is one that is unlikely to erupt again.___

9. crater ___The crater at the top of a volcanic cone is shaped like a bowl.___

10. dormant volcano ___Even though it hasn't erupted recently, a dormant volcano may still erupt.___

Write!

Write your response to the prompt on a separate sheet of paper. Use as many vocabulary words as you can in your writing.

Imagine you are studying a volcano before and after its eruption. Over time, what events and changes can you report?

Volcanoes   27

Write!

Distribute Writing Graphic Organizer: Sequence Chart, Teacher Guide page 83. Tell students to write in the first box of the chart what happens before a volcanic eruption. In the following boxes, they should write in order what happens during an eruption and what happens after an eruption.

Sample Answer

At first, I thought this was an extinct volcano. But then I realized it was a dormant volcano. A week later, the volcano turned into an active volcano. Magma flowed through a fissure in the ground. Soon the volcanic eruption turned violent. Magma pushed up with force. Lava flowed over the surface. Ash shot high into the air. Over time, a huge cone with a crater formed.

TAKE-HOME ACTIVITY

Assign the Take-Home Activity to students for additional practice with the target vocabulary words. The reproducible Take-Home Activity for Lesson 4 is on page 87 of the Teacher Guide.

Take-Home Activity (p. 87)

TAKE HOME 4

magma   lava   fissure   crater   dormant volcano
vent   volcanic eruption   cone   active volcano   extinct volcano

Use vocabulary words to complete the puzzle.

Volcanoes

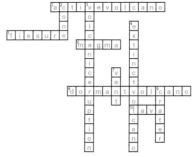

ACROSS

1 a volcano that is erupting or has erupted within the past 10,000 years

5 a long crack in Earth's crust out of which magma flows

6 molten rock below Earth's surface

8 a volcano that is not active or extinct

10 magma that reaches Earth's surface

DOWN

2 a mountain that forms from repeated volcanic eruptions

3 the flowing or bursting out of magma, gases, or ash from a volcano

4 a volcano that has not erupted for 10,000 years

7 an opening of a volcano at the surface

9 a bowl-shaped hole at the top of a volcanic cone

 Tell someone in your family what you have learned about volcanoes.

©Curriculum Associates, LLC *Passwords: Science Vocabulary, Earth Science, Lesson 4*   87

LESSON 5

Changes and Forces in the Rock Cycle

(Student Book pages 28–33)

TARGET VOCABULARY

igneous rock rock formed from magma

sedimentary rock rock formed from tiny bits of other rock

sediment small bits of rock broken off of larger rock

metamorphic rock rock formed when heat, pressure, or chemicals change one kind of rock to another kind

physical weathering the breaking up of rock by wind, rain, or ice

chemical weathering the breaking up of rock by a chemical

erosion the wearing away of rock and sediment

transportation the carrying of rock and sediment to a new place

deposition the dropping of transported rock

rock cycle the slow, but constant, changing of rock from one kind to another

COGNATES

Spanish-speaking students may find a discussion of the similarities and differences between English and Spanish cognates helpful.

English	Spanish
igneous rock	roca ígnea
sedimentary rock	roca sedimentaria
sediment	sedimento
metamorphic rock	roca metamórfica
physical	físico
chemical	químico
erosion	erosión
transportation	transportación
deposition	deposición
rock cycle	ciclo de las rocas

Lesson Summary The rock cycle is the series of changes that rock keeps going through. There are three main classes of rock. Igneous rock forms from volcanic activity; sedimentary rock forms from layers of sediment; and metamorphic rock forms when heat, pressure, or chemicals change one type of rock to another. Physical and chemical weathering break down rock. Erosion occurs, for example, when fast moving water transports weathered rock and deposits it in a new place.

BEFORE READING

Activate Prior Knowledge

Have students make a list of verbs describing what they think can happen to rocks (*break, crack, melt*). Ask students to describe how the rocks may change when they, for example, break, crack, or melt. After students read the lesson, have them compare the changes they read about with those they guessed.

Introduce Target Vocabulary

Tell students they are about to read a selection about the rock cycle. Write the target vocabulary words on the board. Model the pronunciation of each word and have student volunteers repeat the word. Discuss the meaning of each word and, if necessary, write the definition next to the word.

Present Graphic Organizer

Provide each student with a copy of Vocabulary Graphic Organizer: Cycle, Teacher Guide page 79. On the line in the center of the organizer, have students write *The Rock Cycle*. Tell them the top half of the circle represents above the Earth's surface and the bottom half below the Earth's surface. Have them add target vocabulary words inside the circle, in a logical order and placement, as they read the lesson.

Word and Definition Cards
for Lesson 5 are on pages 107 and 108
of the Teacher Guide.

VOCABULARY STRATEGY: Noun Suffix

Ask students what part of speech *erosion, deposition,* and *transportation* are (*nouns*). Ask if students know the verb forms of these words (*erode, deposit, transport*). Have students note that *d* changed to *s* and the *e* was dropped to make the verb *erode* into the noun *erosion.* Ask students for sentences using the verb form of each word. Explain that in English, many nouns are formed by adding the suffix *-ion* to a verb. Have students list some of these words (*action, evaporation, explanation, expansion, precipitation, etc.*). Encourage students to add these words to the suffix chart on page 100 of their book.

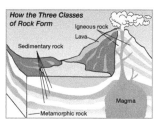

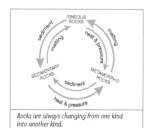

DURING READING

Read the selection aloud to students, stopping at the end of each paragraph or section. Review any words or concepts that students are having trouble with. Remind students that there is a glossary at the back of their book that contains all of the words that appear in boldfaced type in the lesson.

- Discuss the term *weathering*, connecting it to forces of weather—such as wind, rain, temperature changes—as well as moving water and glaciers, plant roots, and human actions. Have students find or draw and label pictures of structures formed by physical weathering—such as buttes—and evidences of chemical weathering—such as caves.

- Explain that *erosion* is a more general term than *transportation*, though both imply the moving of weathered rock. *Erosion* also is "the leftover evidences of rock having been moved away," such as soil erosion. *Deposition* is an opposite of *erosion* and *transportation*.

- Draw a circle on the board. Have students list the three classes of rock (*igneous, sedimentary, and metamorphic*) in any order, and write them on the circle. Then have students explain how a rock could go through the cycle as shown on the board.

Have students read the selection again on their own.

AFTER READING

Review Graphic Organizers

Answer any questions students have about the reading selection. Then have students complete or review their graphic organizer and share it with the class.

Summarize

Have students work together to come up with either a written or an oral summary of the lesson. Encourage students to use the target vocabulary words as the basis of their summary. Have students share their summary with the class.

My Science Vocabulary

Encourage students to turn to My Science Vocabulary on page 95 of the student book and use the space provided to add other words about the rock cycle.

igneous rock   metamorphic rock   erosion   deposition
sedimentary rock   physical weathering   transportation   rock cycle
sediment   chemical weathering

A. *Fill in the blanks with the correct vocabulary word.*

1. rock formed from magma
   i g n e o u s   r o c k

2. the breaking down of rock by chemicals so that the chemical makeup of the rock changes
   c h e m i c a l   w e a t h e r i n g

3. all the changes that rock keeps going through
   r o c k   c y c l e

4. small bits of broken-off, or weathered, rock
   s e d i m e n t

5. rock formed from layers of sediment and other matter, which are squeezed and cemented together
   s e d i m e n t a r y   r o c k

6. the breaking down of rock by wind, rain, or ice so that only the size of the rock changes
   p h y s i c a l   w e a t h e r i n g

7. the wearing away of rocks and sediment by gravity, wind, water, or ice
   e r o s i o n

8. the carrying of rocks and sediment from one place to another
   t r a n s p o r t a t i o n

9. rock formed deep inside Earth by heat and pressure
   m e t a m o r p h i c   r o c k

10. the dropping of rocks and sediment in a new place
    d e p o s i t i o n

igneous rock   metamorphic rock   erosion   deposition
sedimentary rock   physical weathering   transportation   rock cycle
sediment   chemical weathering

B. *Circle the word that makes sense in each sentence. Then write the word.*

1. The breaking down of rock by chemicals is (physical weathering, (chemical weathering)). ___chemical weathering___

2. When a river carries rocks and sediment downstream, the process is called ((transportation), deposition). ___transportation___

3. After the weathering of rock, ((erosion) deposition) by gravity, wind, water, or ice can occur. ___erosion___

4. Rock that hardens from magma is (sedimentary rock, (igneous rock)). ___igneous rock___

5. A solid rock formed from heat and pressure deep inside Earth is (sedimentary rock, (metamorphic rock)). ___metamorphic rock___

6. Tiny bits of broken rock are (rock cycle, (sediment)). ___sediment___

7. When wind or water break down the size of rock, the process is (deposition, (physical weathering)). ___physical weathering___

8. The dropping of sediment in a new place is ((deposition) transportation). ___deposition___

9. A layered rock made up of sediment and bits of shell and tiny bones is (metamorphic rock, (sedimentary rock)). ___sedimentary rock___

10. All the changes that rock keeps going through make up the ((rock cycle) physical weathering). ___rock cycle___

WORD ROOT
The word **igneous** comes from the Latin word **ignis**, meaning "fire."

ACTIVITIES A–D

Encourage students to complete as many of the activities as possible. Remind students that they may refer to the Glossary at the back of their book as they complete the activities. Students may work independently, in small groups, or as a class. When students are done, discuss the answers for each activity.

Extensions

These extension ideas allow you to reuse or expand upon the activities. Share them with students who complete the activities before other students, or have students do them for additional practice with the target vocabulary words.

A Circle the suffixes on the target vocabulary words *(-al, -ary, -ic, -ing, -ous, -ion)*. Look up the suffixes in a dictionary and explain how each suffix changes the word it was added to.

B Write each target vocabulary word that was not used to complete each activity sentence. Use this word to write a sentence that is as close as possible to the original sentence. For example:
1. *The breaking down of rock by wind is physical weathering.*

WORD ROOT

Have students explain how the root *ignis* relates to *igneous rock*. *(Igneous rock forms from fiery hot magma or lava.)* Add that *metamorphic* comes from the Latin word *metamorphosis*, meaning "change." Ask students how that root relates to the meaning. *(Heat and pressure inside Earth change rock into metamorphic rock.)* Have students find the word *sediment* in *sedimentary*.

C Circle the prepositional phrases in the sentences. Not every sentence has a prepositional phrase, but some have more than one. Look for the prepositions *by, from, in, during, under, to, at,* and *of*.

D Write a second sentence that adds more information for each pair of target vocabulary words.

igneous rock	metamorphic rock	erosion	deposition
sedimentary rock	physical weathering	transportation	rock cycle
sediment	chemical weathering		

C. Choose the correct vocabulary word to complete each sentence.

1. Rock that formed in layers under the sea is ___sedimentary rock___.

2. When a river carrying sediment slows down, ___deposition___ takes place.

3. New igneous, sedimentary, and metamorphic rocks are always forming because of the ___rock cycle___.

4. The process of ___physical weathering___ changes only the size of the pieces of rock.

5. One example of erosion is ___transportation___, the carrying of rocks and sediment to a new place.

6. If metamorphic rock melts into magma, it can become ___igneous rock___.

7. Wind, water, and ice cause the ___erosion___ of weathered rock.

8. If the chemical makeup of a rock changes, the change may have been caused by ___chemical weathering___.

9. Great heat and pressure deep inside Earth can change igneous rock to ___metamorphic rock___.

10. Sedimentary rock is formed from ___sediment___ and bits of shells or bones.

 32
Changes and Forces in the Rock Cycle

---

igneous rock	metamorphic rock	erosion	deposition
sedimentary rock	physical weathering	transportation	rock cycle
sediment	chemical weathering		

Students' answers will vary.

D. Use each pair of words in a sentence.

1. physical weathering, chemical weathering
   In physical weathering, only the rock's size changes, but in chemical weathering, the rock's makeup changes.

2. rock cycle, metamorphic rock
   During the rock cycle, metamorphic rock can change into a new class of rock.

3. sedimentary rock, igneous rock
   If tiny bits break off from igneous rock, that sediment can become part of a sedimentary rock.

4. sediment, erosion
   Gravity, wind, water, and ice can cause the erosion of sediment.

5. transportation, deposition
   A stream can be a force of transportation by carrying sediment, as well as a force of deposition, by dropping sediment.

 Write!
Write your response to the prompt on a separate sheet of paper. Use as many vocabulary words as you can in your writing.
If you could follow a sample of rock for billions of years, what changes might that rock go through?

Changes and Forces in the Rock Cycle 33

Write!

Distribute Writing Graphic Organizer: Sequence Chart, Teacher Guide page 83. Tell students to write in the first box of the chart a class of rock and a beginning event in the rock cycle. In the following boxes, they should write in order the events and changes that would occur to that rock.

Sample Answer

Long ago, sediment fell on the ocean floor. The sediment became sedimentary rock. This rock was buried deep and turned into metamorphic rock. Following the rock cycle, this rock melted into magma. The magma became igneous rock. Physical weathering broke up the igneous rock. Erosion by wind, transportation by a river, and deposition at the mouth of the river changed the rock. There, chemical weathering changed the rock to a new rock.

TAKE-HOME ACTIVITY

Assign the Take-Home Activity to students for additional practice with the target vocabulary words. The reproducible Take-Home Activity for Lesson 5 is on page 88 of the Teacher Guide.

TAKE HOME 5

igneous rock	metamorphic rock	erosion	deposition
sedimentary rock	physical weathering	transportation	rock cycle
sediment	chemical weathering		

Use vocabulary words to complete the puzzle.

Changes and Forces in the Rock Cycle

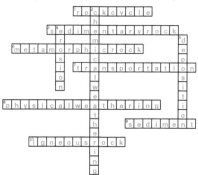

ACROSS

1 all the changes rock goes through
3 rock formed from layers of sediment
6 rock formed from heat and pressure
7 the carrying of rock to a new place
8 the breaking down of rock into small pieces
9 bits of rock broken off from larger rock
10 rock formed from hardened magma

DOWN

2 the breaking down of rock by chemicals
4 the wearing away of rocks and sediment by gravity, wind, water, and ice
5 the dropping of rocks and sediment in a new place

 Tell someone in your family what you have learned about changes and forces in the rock cycle.

LESSON 6

Fossils

(Student Book pages 34–39)

Lesson Summary Fossils are remains or traces of ancient organisms. Fossilization occurs, for example, when real remains are preserved in rock or replaced by minerals. Other types of fossils include impressions left when a plant is pressed in mud and decays, hollow molds formed when mud hardens around an organism that dissolves or decays, and casts formed when new minerals fill a mold. A trace fossil is evidence of the movement of an animal. Fossils taken together make up the fossil record.

TARGET VOCABULARY

fossil the remains or traces of ancient plants or animals

fossilization the process of becoming a fossil

decay to rot

preserved kept whole

dissolve to break down and wash away

impression an image pressed into matter

mold a hollow shape that can be filled

cast a fossil that forms when minerals fill a mold

trace fossil marks made by the movement of an ancient animal

fossil record all fossils taken together that show the history of life on Earth

COGNATES

Spanish-speaking students may find a discussion of the similarities and differences between English and Spanish cognates helpful.

English	Spanish
fossil	fósil
dissolve	disolverse
impression	impresión
mold	molde

BEFORE READING

Activate Prior Knowledge

Have students respond to the following questions: How could you find out what life was like yesterday? 100 years ago? 1,000 years ago? One million years ago? Write some of the answers to one million years ago on the board. Have students add to this list as they read the lesson.

Introduce Target Vocabulary

Tell students they are about to read a selection about fossils. Write the target vocabulary words on the board. Model the pronunciation of each word and have student volunteers repeat the word. Discuss the meaning of each word and, if necessary, write the definition next to the word.

Present Graphic Organizer

Provide each student with a copy of Vocabulary Graphic Organizer: Venn Diagram, Teacher Guide page 77. Differentiate for students the meaning of *remains* ("actual pieces") and *traces* ("other evidence"). Have students title one circle *Real Remains* and one *Traces*. As they read the lesson, have students write the target vocabulary words under the title that seems most appropriate. Point out that the overlap of the circles is for words that fit under both titles.

Word and Definition Cards
for Lesson 6 are on pages 109 and 110
of the Teacher Guide.

VOCABULARY STRATEGY: Word Families

Point out that many of the target vocabulary words include the word *fossil*. Have students explain how the word *fossil* is used differently in the following vocabulary words: *fossil (noun—the object)*, *fossilization (noun—the process)*, *trace fossil (noun used* *with an adjective to make a compound noun)*, and *fossil record (noun used as an adjective to make a compound noun)*. Ask students what the verb based on *fossil* is *(fossilize)*. Tell them that *fossiliferous* is an adjective that means "having many fossils."

Fossils

fossil   decay   dissolve   mold   trace fossil
fossilization   preserved   impression   cast   fossil record

You know what dinosaurs looked like. How is that possible?
How do people know about plants and animals that lived long ago?
Read this selection to find out.

Fossils

A **fossil** is the remains or traces of an ancient plant or animal. The process of forming fossils is **fossilization**. Fossilization occurs in different ways.

Fossil Remains

A few fossils are real parts of animals' bodies. When animals die, the soft parts of their bodies **decay**, or rot, quickly. But the hard parts, such as bones, teeth, and shells, remain. Those parts get buried in mud or sand, which slowly hardens into rock. The hard parts get trapped inside the rock.

Sometimes an animal's entire body becomes a fossil. These animals were **preserved**, or kept whole, in rock, tar, or ice.

Most fossils are not real remains, but they can be exact copies. Water can **dissolve**, or break down and wash away, all or part of a dead plant or animal buried under the ground. Minerals in the water then replace the dissolving plant or animal parts bit by bit. What is left is a copy, in rock, of the original plant or animal.

Fossilization

A fish dies in the ocean.

The soft parts of the fish decay.

Fossilized bones remain.

These insects were caught in sticky sap that hardened into a stone called amber.

Fossil Traces

An **impression** is an image pressed into matter. An impression is different from remains because it shows only one surface of the plant or animal. For example, a leaf may be pressed into mud. The mud will harden into rock. The leaf will decay. But the shape of the leaf will remain in the rock.

A fossil impression is a type of mold. A **mold** is a hollow shape that can be filled. Suppose an animal becomes buried in mud. The animal decays or dissolves, and the mud becomes rock. Only the hollow shape of the animal will be left in the rock.

If minerals later fill the mold and harden, a **cast** forms. The cast looks like the actual animal but is made of rock.

A **trace fossil** is the marks made by the movement of an ancient animal, such as dinosaur tracks. Tracks may show the shape of the animal's feet and suggest how the animal moved. Tracks are also a kind of mold or impression.

Using Fossil Evidence

Scientists use fossils to see what life was like long ago. All the fossils taken together make up the **fossil record**. The fossil record shows the history of life on Earth in ages past.

Impression of a Fossil Fern

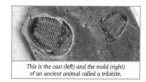
This is the cast (left) and the mold (right) of an ancient animal called a trilobite.

Dinosaur Fossil

My Science Vocabulary
Go to page 95 to list other words you have learned about fossils.

DURING READING

Read the selection aloud to students, stopping at the end of each paragraph or section. Review any words or concepts that students are having trouble with. Remind students that there is a glossary at the back of their book that contains all of the words that appear in boldfaced type in the lesson.

- Discuss the diagram of fossilization on page 34. Ask volunteers to explain the process aloud. Then ask how the fossil might be found. (*The sea could dry out and the seabed rock could weather. Scientists might dig it up under water, etc.*)

- With clay or claylike material, make an impression of an object. Fill a hollow shape, such as a small paper cup, with clay to demonstrate a mold, and push the clay carefully out to show a cast. Pressing down to make an impression, walk your fingers across a smoothed piece of clay to make a trace fossil. As you demonstrate, have students describe what you are doing.

- Show students a geologic time-scale chart of the fossil record. Discuss the types of things the fossil record shows.

Have students read the selection again on their own.

AFTER READING

Review Graphic Organizers

Answer any questions students have about the reading selection. Then have students complete or review their graphic organizer and share it with the class.

Summarize

Have students work together to come up with either a written or an oral summary of the lesson. Encourage students to use the target vocabulary words as the basis of their summary. Have students share their summary with the class.

My Science Vocabulary

Encourage students to turn to My Science Vocabulary on page 95 of the student book and use the space provided to add other words about fossils.

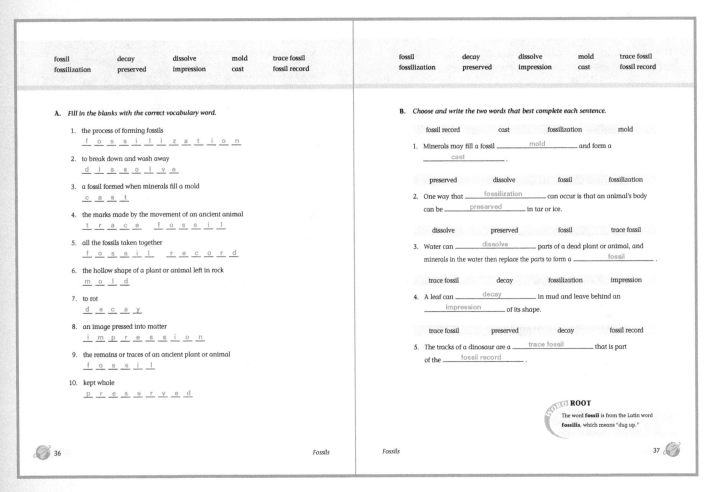

ACTIVITIES A–D

Encourage students to complete as many of the activities as possible. Remind students that they may refer to the Glossary at the back of their book as they complete the activities. Students may work independently, in small groups, or as a class. When students are done, discuss the answers for each activity.

Extensions

These extension ideas allow you to reuse or expand upon the activities. Share them with students who complete the activities before other students, or have students do them for additional practice with the target vocabulary words.

A Group all or some of the target vocabulary words into pairs that seem to go best together. Explain the choices.

B Circle all the nouns and underline all the verbs in the completed sentences.

C Combine the ideas from each pair of sentences into one sentence.

D Change each sentence into a question that has the target vocabulary word as its answer.

WORD ROOT

Have students determine how the word *fossil* relates to what a fossil fuel is *(a fuel, or energy source, made of ancient remains found in the ground that must be dug up or somehow brought up to the surface).*

fossil   decay   dissolve   mold   trace fossil
fossilization   preserved   impression   cast   fossil record

C. *Write the vocabulary word that best completes each pair of sentences.*

1. Life in ages past is recorded in the _____fossil record_____ .
   All fossils taken together make up the _____fossil record_____ .

2. Dead plants and animals _____decay_____ over time.
   Soft body parts _____decay_____ quickly.

3. The remains of an ancient animal may become a _____fossil_____ .
   A mold is a _____fossil_____ that shows only the traces of an ancient plant or animal.

4. Water can _____dissolve_____ all or part of a dead plant or animal.
   Minerals replace the plant or animal parts that _____dissolve_____ .

5. The minerals in a _____cast_____ have filled up a hollow in rock.
   A _____cast_____ is made from a mold.

6. During the process of _____fossilization_____ , fossils form.
   Molds, casts, and trace fossils are all the result of _____fossilization_____ .

7. One type of _____trace fossil_____ is an animal's tracks.
   Scientists can learn how an animal moved through its _____trace fossil_____ .

8. An image pressed into matter is an _____impression_____ .
   A fossil _____impression_____ is a type of mold.

9. Animal fossils are bones, teeth, or shells that are often _____preserved_____ in rock.
   Sometimes an animal's entire body is _____preserved_____ in ice or tar.

10. A hollow space that can fill with new rock is a _____mold_____ .
    A fossil cast forms in a _____mold_____ .

---

fossil   decay   dissolve   mold   trace fossil
fossilization   preserved   impression   cast   fossil record

Students' answers will vary.

D. *Use each word in a sentence that shows you understand the meaning of the word.*

1. trace fossil _If you find the tracks of a dinosaur, you have found a trace fossil._

2. decay _A leaf can decay and leave an impression in mud._

3. mold _A hollow mold can fill with minerals that harden into rock._

4. fossil record _Scientists study the fossil record to see what life was like long ago._

5. fossil _A fossil is often found in rock._

6. preserved _Hard parts of animals, such as teeth and bones, may be preserved as fossils._

7. dissolve _Water can dissolve parts of a dead animal buried under the ground._

8. fossilization _Because of fossilization, we know about life long ago._

9. cast _When minerals fill a fossil mold and harden, a cast forms._

10. impression _An impression could show the veins of an ancient leaf._

Write!
Write your response to the prompt on a separate sheet of paper. Use as many vocabulary words as you can in your writing.
What kinds of things might you find if you went looking for signs of life long ago?

Write!

Distribute Writing Graphic Organizer: Narrative Map, Teacher Guide page 82. Have students work with a partner or in a small group to brainstorm ideas for writing. They should list themselves as the main character for this first-person narrative. Setting(s) will include all the places they travel. Main events will include what will occur.

Sample Answer

    If I went looking for signs of life long ago, I would find a place where fossilization had happened. In ice, I might find an animal preserved. On an ancient seabed, I could find a mold with a cast of a shell. I would not see the animal decay or parts of the shell dissolve. But I would see the fossil. I would look for a trace fossil of dinosaur footprints in long-ago soft mud. I could check the fossil record to learn more about my finds.

TAKE-HOME ACTIVITY

Assign the Take-Home Activity to students for additional practice with the target vocabulary words. The reproducible Take-Home Activity for Lesson 6 is on page 89 of the Teacher Guide.

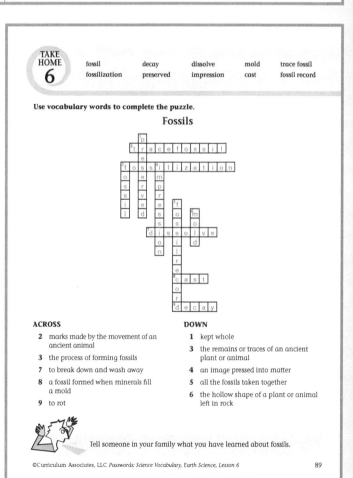

TAKE HOME 6

fossil   decay   dissolve   mold   trace fossil
fossilization   preserved   impression   cast   fossil record

Use vocabulary words to complete the puzzle.

Fossils

ACROSS
2 marks made by the movement of an ancient animal
3 the process of forming fossils
7 to break down and wash away
8 a fossil formed when minerals fill a mold
9 to rot

DOWN
1 kept whole
3 the remains or traces of an ancient plant or animal
4 an image pressed into matter
5 all the fossils taken together
6 the hollow shape of a plant or animal left in rock

Tell someone in your family what you have learned about fossils.

LESSON 7

Features of Minerals

(Student Book pages 40–45)

TARGET VOCABULARY

mineral a solid with no living matter formed naturally in the earth

inorganic having no living matter

element a mineral made up of only one type of matter

compound a mineral made of two or more elements

crystal a regular, repeating, smooth-sided structure

cleavage the quality of a mineral to split along a smooth surface

streak the color of the powder left when a mineral is scratched on a special plate

luster the shine or lack of shine of a mineral

metallic shiny like a metal

nonmetallic not shiny, like a nonmetal

COGNATES

Spanish-speaking students may find a discussion of the similarities and differences between English and Spanish cognates helpful.

English	Spanish
mineral	mineral
inorganic	inorgánico
element	elemento
compound	compuesto
crystal	cristal
luster	lustre
metallic	metálico

VOCABULARY STRATEGY: Multimeaning Words

Remind students that words often have more than one meaning. The correct meaning depends on the context in which the word is used. For example, in science, some words take on a specific meaning that is related to the general meaning of the word. Ask students what *space* means in general (*an open area, a gap*) and what it means in science (*outer space*). Have students look up in a dictionary the target vocabulary words that take on a specific meaning related to mineral identification: *cleavage, streak, luster, metallic,* and *nonmetallic.* Discuss how the more general meaning of these terms relates to the mineral characteristic.

Lesson Summary A mineral is an inorganic solid with a specific chemical composition and crystal structure that is found in the earth. An element has one type of matter, and a compound has more than one element. Features such as the crystal structure, cleavage, streak, and luster help identify a mineral. Cleavage is the breaking of a mineral along a smooth plane. The streak is the color of the powder left by scratching a mineral on a streak plate. Luster, or shine, can be metallic or nonmetallic.

BEFORE READING

Activate Prior Knowledge

Bring in some common rocks and minerals, or pictures of minerals. Ask students to list ways they could describe the minerals to help someone else recognize them. Write the list on the board or have each student write the list. As students read the lesson, have them add to the list.

Introduce Target Vocabulary

Tell students they are about to read a selection about features of minerals. Write the target vocabulary words on the board. Model the pronunciation of each word and have student volunteers repeat the word. Discuss the meaning of each word and, if necessary, write the definition next to the word.

Present Graphic Organizer

Provide each student with a copy of Vocabulary Graphic Organizer: Word Web, Teacher Guide page 76. Have students write *Mineral* in the center circle of the web. As they read the lesson, have students group related target vocabulary words in the outer circles. Have them write a phrase next to each circle that explains why they grouped the words together. Tell them they may add circles, if necessary.

Word and Definition Cards
for Lesson 7 are on pages 111 and 112
of the Teacher Guide.

Features of Minerals

| mineral | element | crystal | streak | metallic |
| inorganic | compound | cleavage | luster | nonmetallic |

You pick up a mineral and want to know what it is. What will help you identify the mineral? Read this selection to see if you guessed all the features.

Features of Minerals

A **mineral** is a solid that is formed naturally in the earth. All minerals are **inorganic**. They have no living matter. Each mineral has a specific chemical makeup and structure. Quartz and pyrite are common minerals.

Quartz

Pyrite

Elements and Compounds

Some minerals are elements. An **element** is made up of only one type of matter. An element cannot be broken down into simpler substances. For example, gold is an element.

Most minerals are compounds. A **compound** is made of two or more elements. Table salt is a compound. It is made up of the elements sodium and chloride.

Identifying a Mineral

Minerals can be identified by their color and hardness. All minerals also have a crystal structure. A **crystal** is a regular, repeating shape with smooth sides. Many crystals are very tiny, but some are large enough to see easily. The shape of the crystals helps identify a mineral. Crystals of the compound salt are cubes. Cubes have six flat sides that are equal in length and width.

Common Crystal Shapes

 40

Features of Minerals

Cleavage, Streak, and Luster

Some minerals have cleavage. **Cleavage** is the ability of a mineral to split along a smooth inner surface, or plane. When hit, minerals with cleavage break smoothly along one or more planes. Minerals without cleavage shatter into jagged edges or odd shapes.

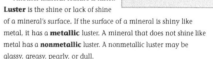

Mica's cleavage is on one plane.   Halite's cleavage is on three planes.

Another feature of a mineral is found by scratching the mineral on a special white plate. The color of the powder left from the scratch is the **streak** of the mineral. The streak can be a different color from the mineral itself. For example, a black mineral can have a reddish brown streak.

Another mineral feature is luster. **Luster** is the shine or lack of shine of a mineral's surface. If the surface of a mineral is shiny like metal, it has a **metallic** luster. A mineral that does not shine like metal has a **nonmetallic** luster. A nonmetallic luster may be glassy, greasy, pearly, or dull.

Testing for Streak

 My Science Vocabulary
Go to page 96 to list other words you have learned about features of minerals.

Features of Minerals

41

DURING READING

Read the selection aloud to students, stopping at the end of each paragraph or section. Review any words or concepts that students are having trouble with. Remind students that there is a glossary at the back of their book that contains all of the words that appear in boldfaced type in the lesson.

- Point out that *inorganic* uses the prefix *in-*, or "not." *Organic* means "relating to living things." Carbon is the only organic element. All others are inorganic.

- Review that a compound has more than one element, and an element is one of over 100 substances that cannot normally be broken down and keep its properties. Many are solid minerals, but some are liquids (mercury) and gases (oxygen). Ask students to name some elements.

- Refer students to the crystal shapes on page 40 and ask which shows salt *(second from top)*. Have students look at table salt crystals using a magnifying glass or microscope and describe what they see.

Have students read the selection again on their own.

AFTER READING

Review Graphic Organizers

Answer any questions students have about the reading selection. Then have students complete or review their graphic organizer and share it with the class.

Summarize

Have students work together to come up with either a written or an oral summary of the lesson. Encourage students to use the target vocabulary words as the basis of their summary. Have students share their summary with the class.

My Science Vocabulary

Encourage students to turn to My Science Vocabulary on page 96 of the student book and use the space provided to add other words about features of minerals.

Features of Minerals

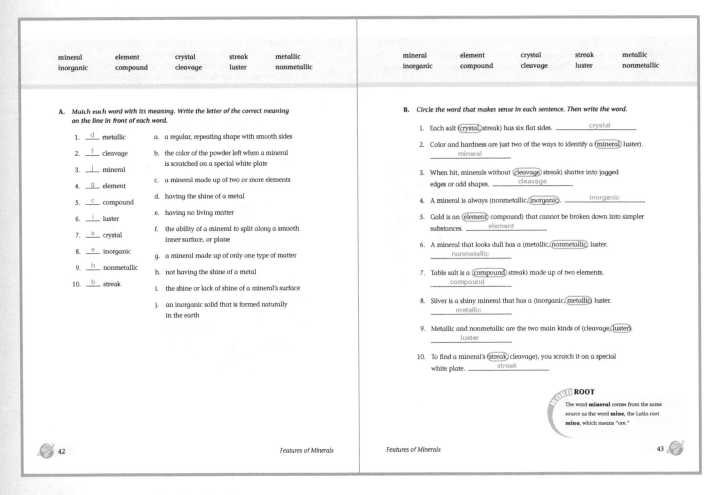

A. Match each word with its meaning. Write the letter of the correct meaning on the line in front of each word.

1. __d__ metallic
2. __f__ cleavage
3. __j__ mineral
4. __g__ element
5. __c__ compound
6. __i__ luster
7. __a__ crystal
8. __e__ inorganic
9. __h__ nonmetallic
10. __b__ streak

a. a regular, repeating shape with smooth sides
b. the color of the powder left when a mineral is scratched on a special white plate
c. a mineral made up of two or more elements
d. having the shine of a metal
e. having no living matter
f. the ability of a mineral to split along a smooth inner surface, or plane
g. a mineral made up of only one type of matter
h. not having the shine of a metal
i. the shine or lack of shine of a mineral's surface
j. an inorganic solid that is formed naturally in the earth

B. Circle the word that makes sense in each sentence. Then write the word.

1. Each salt (crystal, streak) has six flat sides. _____ crystal
2. Color and hardness are just two of the ways to identify a (mineral, luster). _____ mineral
3. When hit, minerals without (cleavage, streak) shatter into jagged edges or odd shapes. _____ cleavage
4. A mineral is always (nonmetallic, inorganic). _____ inorganic
5. Gold is an (element, compound) that cannot be broken down into simpler substances. _____ element
6. A mineral that looks dull has a (metallic, nonmetallic) luster. _____ nonmetallic
7. Table salt is a (compound, streak) made up of two elements. _____ compound
8. Silver is a shiny mineral that has a (inorganic, metallic) luster. _____ metallic
9. Metallic and nonmetallic are the two main kinds of (cleavage, luster). _____ luster
10. To find a mineral's (streak, cleavage), you scratch it on a special white plate. _____ streak

WORD ROOT

The word **mineral** comes from the same source as the word **mine**, the Latin root **mina**, which means "ore."

ACTIVITIES A–D

Encourage students to complete as many of the activities as possible. Remind students that they may refer to the Glossary at the back of their book as they complete the activities. Students may work independently, in small groups, or as a class. When students are done, discuss the answers for each activity.

Extensions

These extension ideas allow you to reuse or expand upon the activities. Share them with students who complete the activities before other students, or have students do them for additional practice with the target vocabulary words.

A Put the target vocabulary words in alphabetical order.

B Make four columns and group the target vocabulary words into those with one syllable, two syllables, three syllables, and four syllables.

WORD ROOT

Explain that an ore is a mineral that can be taken from the ground. Ask students to explain how *mine* relates to the word *mineral*. ("*To mine*" is to "*free metals, salts, or other minerals from the ground.*" A "*mine*" is a "*place where mining is done.*")

C Circle all the target vocabulary words that are nouns. Draw a line under each vocabulary word that is an adjective. Add one of the circled nouns after each adjective to form a phrase that makes sense (*metallic luster, inorganic compound, etc.*).

D Use a sample of a mineral, a picture of a mineral, or make up a mineral, and write sentences using the pairs of target vocabulary words to describe this mineral.

mineral	element	crystal	streak	metallic
inorganic	compound	cleavage	luster	nonmetallic

C. *Write the vocabulary word that best completes each pair of sentences.*

1. There are at least two elements in a _____ compound _____
   Sodium and chloride are elements in the ____ compound ____ called salt.

2. A shiny luster like that of metal is described as ____ metallic ____ .
   Gold is shiny and has a ____ metallic ____ luster.

3. A diamond is a very hard ____ mineral ____ that is found in the earth.
   Quartz is a common ____ mineral ____ .

4. Gold is shiny like metal, but quartz has a glassy ____ luster ____
   Like gold, silver has a metallic ____ luster ____ .

5. The color of the scratch a mineral makes on a special white plate is its
   _____ streak _____ .
   A black mineral can have a brown ____ streak ____ .

6. If something has no living matter it is ____ inorganic ____ .
   All minerals are ____ inorganic ____ .

7. A cube is the shape of each ____ crystal ____ in salt.
   The sides of a ____ crystal ____ are smooth and have repeating shapes.

8. A mineral with only one type of matter is an ____ element ____ .
   Every compound has more than one ____ element ____ .

9. A mineral with a dull luster is ____ nonmetallic ____ .
   A mineral with a ____ nonmetallic ____ luster isn't shiny like metal.

10. The breaking of a mineral on a smooth inner surface is
    _____ cleavage _____ .
    The ____ cleavage ____ of a mineral shows up when
    the mineral is pulled apart or hit.

---

mineral	element	crystal	streak	metallic
inorganic	compound	cleavage	luster	nonmetallic

Students' answers will vary.

D. *Use each pair of words in a sentence.*

1. crystal, cleavage
   All minerals have a crystal shape, but only some minerals have cleavage.

2. luster, streak
   The luster of a mineral and its streak help identify the mineral.

3. metallic, nonmetallic
   Minerals that shine like a metal have a metallic luster, and those that
   do not shine that way have a nonmetallic luster.

4. mineral, inorganic
   A mineral is always inorganic.

5. element, compound
   An element has only one type of matter, but a compound has at least
   two elements.

Write!
Write your response to the prompt on a separate sheet of paper.
Use as many vocabulary words as you can in your writing.

Suppose you found a sample of an unusual mineral. Tell how you could
identify exactly what the mineral was.

Write!

Distribute Writing Graphic Organizer: Idea Wheel, Teacher Guide page 81. Tell students to write *Identifying a Mineral* in the center of the wheel. Then on the spokes of the wheel, they should write the tests they would use to identify the mineral. Tell students they may add spokes to the wheel, if necessary.

Sample Answer

First, I would make sure the mineral was inorganic. Then I'd look at the color and hardness. I would decide whether the luster was metallic or nonmetallic. I would test for the streak. I would then try to peel or break a sample to see if it had cleavage. I would look for small or large crystals. Then I would check a book to get the name of what the mineral might be. Finally, I would check to see whether the name meant it was an element or a compound.

TAKE-HOME ACTIVITY

Assign the Take-Home Activity to students for additional practice with the target vocabulary words. The reproducible Take-Home Activity for Lesson 7 is on page 90 of the Teacher Guide.

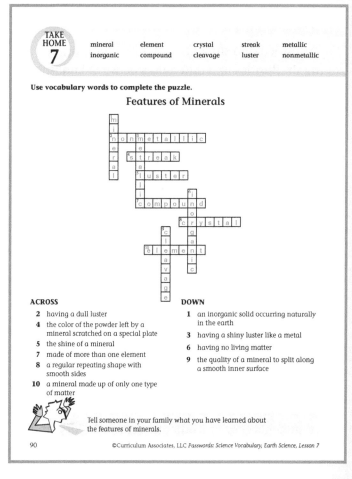

TAKE HOME 7

mineral	element	crystal	streak	metallic
inorganic	compound	cleavage	luster	nonmetallic

Use vocabulary words to complete the puzzle.

Features of Minerals

ACROSS
2 having a dull luster
4 the color of the powder left by a mineral scratched on a special plate
5 the shine of a mineral
7 made of more than one element
8 a regular repeating shape with smooth sides
10 a mineral made up of only one type of matter

DOWN
1 an inorganic solid occurring naturally in the earth
3 having a shiny luster like a metal
6 having no living matter
9 the quality of a mineral to split along a smooth inner surface

Tell someone in your family what you have learned about the features of minerals.

90   ©Curriculum Associates, LLC *Passwords: Science Vocabulary, Earth Science, Lesson 7*

LESSON 8

Protecting Earth's Resources

(Student Book pages 46–51)

TARGET VOCABULARY

natural resource something found in nature that people use

inexhaustible resource a resource that can be used over and over

renewable resource a resource that can be replaced

nonrenewable resource a resource that cannot be replaced

fossil fuel coal, oil, or natural gas

conservation saving resources by using less

recycling making new goods from used goods

preservation saving resources by not using or not polluting them

pollutant a chemical harmful to natural resources

acid rain a pollutant of acid mixed with rain

COGNATES

Spanish-speaking students may find a discussion of the similarities and differences between English and Spanish cognates helpful.

English	Spanish
natural resource	recurso natural
renewable resource	recurso renovable
fossil	fósil
preservation	preservación
conservation	conservación
recycling	reciclaje
acid	ácida

Lesson Summary Natural resources, such as air, water, oil, plants, and animals, are things found in nature that people use. A few resources, such as sunlight, are inexhaustible and cannot be used up. Renewable resources, such as wood, can be replaced as they are used, but nonrenewable resources, such as fossil fuels, cannot. Conservation, or using less of a resource, is aided by recycling. People practice preservation by not using resources and by protecting resources from pollutants, such as acid rain.

BEFORE READING

Activate Prior Knowledge

Have students brainstorm a list of things from nature that people use. Then ask them to put the items in one of the following columns: "Cannot Be Used Up," "Can Be Used and Replaced," "Can Be Used But Not Replaced." Have them adjust their lists as they learn more about resources from the lesson.

Introduce Target Vocabulary

Tell students they are about to read a selection about protecting Earth's resources. Write the target vocabulary words on the board. Model the pronunciation of each word and have student volunteers repeat the word. Discuss the meaning of each word and, if necessary, write the definition next to the word.

Present Graphic Organizer

Provide each student with a copy of Vocabulary Graphic Organizer: Four Square, Teacher Guide page 78. In the center, have students write *Natural Resource*. Have students label the boxes: *Type, Saving, Harmful,* and *Helpful*. As students read the lesson, have them put the target vocabulary words in the correct box or boxes.

> Word and Definition Cards
> for Lesson 8 are on pages 113 and 114
> of the Teacher Guide.

VOCABULARY STRATEGY: Word Parts

Prefixes, suffixes, and roots are small word parts that make it easier to understand a longer word. Have a student write the word *inexhaustible* on the board. With students, break the word into the parts: *in-* (not), *exhaust* (use up), *-ible* (able). Have students state the definition (*"not able to be used up"*). Have students examine other target vocabulary words. *Renewable: re-* (again), *new* (new, lately made) *-able* (able to be); "able to be made new again." *Nonrenewable: non-* (not) *renewable* (see *renewable*); "not able to be made new again." Point out that *preservation* combines the root *servare* meaning "protect" with *pre-* meaning "before"; *conservation* uses *servare* with *con-* meaning "with." Encourage students to add these words to the root words and prefix and suffix charts, page 99 and 100.

Protecting Earth's Resources

The reproduced student book spread:

LESSON 8

natural resource   nonrenewable resource   recycling   pollutant
inexhaustible resource   fossil fuel   preservation   acid rain
renewable resource   conservation

Today, you hear a lot in the news about using up Earth's natural resources. What kinds of resources are in danger? How can you help save them? Read this selection to answer these questions about resources.

Protecting Earth's Resources

Natural Resources

A **natural resource** is something found in nature that people use. Air, water, oil, plants, and animals are examples of natural resources. An **inexhaustible resource** is a resource that can be used over and over without being used up. Sunlight, for example, is an inexhaustible resource. No matter how much sunlight people use, there is always more.

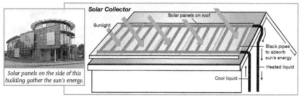

Solar Collector

Solar panels on the side of this building gather the sun's energy.

A **renewable resource** is one that can be replaced as it is used. Food and wood are renewable resources. New food can be grown. New forests can be planted.

A **nonrenewable resource** is a resource that cannot be replaced once it is used up. Fossil fuels are nonrenewable resources. A **fossil fuel** is an energy source formed from decayed plants and animals. Fossil fuels include coal, oil, and natural gas. The fossil fuels used today began forming millions of years ago.

 46

Protecting Earth's Resources

Ways That People Can Help

Conservation is the protection of natural resources by using less of them. For example, by lowering the heat in a building, people use less fuel. More fuel is saved for the future.

Recycling is a method of conservation. **Recycling** means using materials from used goods to make new goods. Instead of throwing plastic bottles into the trash, people recycle them. The plastic goes to a factory to be used to make new plastic.

Preservation is the protection of natural resources by not using them at all or by keeping them clean. People may preserve a forest by not cutting down its trees. People may pass laws to keep a source of water clean.

Pollutants

A **pollutant** is a chemical that results from human activities and that harms natural resources. Pollutants from factories can make the air dirty. Pollutants from farming can seep into the water.

One type of pollutant is the acid in smoke from factories. An acid is a type of chemical. When this acid mixes with rainwater, it forms **acid rain**. Acid rain can kill fish and trees. It can also break down rock. Keeping harmful acids out of factory smoke can prevent the damage caused by acid rain.

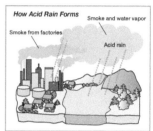

How Acid Rain Forms

 My Science Vocabulary
Go to page 96 to list other words you have learned about protecting Earth's resources.

Protecting Earth's Resources 47

DURING READING

Read the selection aloud to students, stopping at the end of each paragraph or section. Review any words or concepts that students are having trouble with. Remind students that there is a glossary at the back of their book that contains all of the words that appear in boldfaced type in the lesson.

- Have students reread and define the first part of all the compound target vocabulary words that include the word *resource*, such as *natural (from nature); inexhaustible (not able to be used up); renewable (able to be replaced); nonrenewable (not able to be replaced).*

- Hold up a sheet of paper. Ask students what action would be preservation of the paper (*save it in a safe place*), conservation of it (*cut it in half and use only half*), and recycling it (*use it and put it in a recycle bin*).

- Point out the general definition of *pollute* ("to make dirty") and explain that pollution makes soil, water, and air dirty. Therefore, a pollutant can be a solid, a liquid, or a gas. Ask students how these substances might get into soil, water, and air.

Have students read the selection again on their own.

AFTER READING

Review Graphic Organizers

Answer any questions students have about the reading selection. Then have students complete or review their graphic organizer and share it with the class.

Summarize

Have students work together to come up with either a written or an oral summary of the lesson. Encourage students to use the target vocabulary words as the basis of their summary. Have students share their summary with the class.

My Science Vocabulary

Encourage students to turn to My Science Vocabulary on page 96 of the student book and use the space provided to add other words about protecting Earth's resources.

Protecting Earth's Resources

natural resource   nonrenewable resource   recycling   pollutant
inexhaustible resource   fossil fuel   preservation   acid rain
renewable resource   conservation

A. Match each word with its meaning. Write the letter of the correct meaning on the line in front of each word.

1. __c__ fossil fuel
2. __j__ renewable resource
3. __d__ recycling
4. __e__ conservation
5. __i__ nonrenewable resource
6. __g__ pollutant
7. __a__ natural resource
8. __h__ acid rain
9. __b__ preservation
10. __f__ inexhaustible resource

a. something found in nature that people use, such as air, sunlight, plants, and water

b. the protection of natural resources by not using them at all or by keeping them clean

c. an energy source formed from decayed plants and animals

d. using materials from used goods to make new goods

e. the protection of natural resources by using less of them

f. a resource that can be used over and over without being used up

g. a chemical from human activities that harms natural resources

h. a pollutant made of acid mixed with rainwater

i. a resource that cannot be replaced once it is used up

j. a resource that can be replaced as it is used

 48   *Protecting Earth's Resources*

---

natural resource   nonrenewable resource   recycling   pollutant
inexhaustible resource   fossil fuel   preservation   acid rain
renewable resource   conservation

B. Circle the word that makes sense in each sentence. Then write the word.

1. Using old goods to make new goods is (preservation, (recycling)).
   __recycling__

2. Sunlight is a truly ((inexhaustible resource) nonrenewable resource) because it can be used over and over without being used up.
   __inexhaustible resource__

3. A chemical that dirties air or water is a (preservation, (pollutant)).
   __pollutant__

4. When rainwater mixes with acid from factory smoke, ((acid rain) fossil fuel) can form. __acid rain__

5. Setting a resource aside for later use is ((preservation), recycling).
   __preservation__

6. Water is a ((natural resource) pollutant) that people use.
   __natural resource__

7. Since oil is a fossil fuel that began forming millions of years ago, it is a ((nonrenewable resource) renewable resource). __nonrenewable resource__

8. Natural gas is a ((fossil fuel) renewable resource). __fossil fuel__

9. When practicing ((conservation), pollutant), people use less of a resource now so that more is left for the future. __conservation__

10. Food is a ((renewable resource) nonrenewable resource) because new food can be grown. __renewable resource__

ROOT
The word **fuel** comes from the Latin root **focus**, which means "fire or hearth."

Protecting Earth's Resources   49

ACTIVITIES A–D

Encourage students to complete as many of the activities as possible. Remind students that they may refer to the Glossary at the back of their book as they complete the activities. Students may work independently, in small groups, or as a class. When students are done, discuss the answers for each activity.

Extensions

These extension ideas allow you to reuse or expand upon the activities. Share them with students who complete the activities before other students, or have students do them for additional practice with the target vocabulary words.

A Find antonyms for some of the target vocabulary words *(renewable resource—nonrenewable resource; preservation—destruction, natural resource—humanmade resource; etc.)*

B Divide each target vocabulary word into syllables by drawing a line between the syllables.

C Use the Internet or other sources to find or draw pictures to illustrate the meaning of each target vocabulary word. Write a sentence about each picture using the vocabulary word.

D Choose five sentences. These sentences are the answers. Write a question for each answer.

WORD ROOT

To help students understand how the root word relates to the word, point out that a fuel, such as wood, is an energy source that can be used to make a fire. Then have students use a dictionary or other source to find out what the fossil fuel coal is formed from *(the remains of ancient plants)*.

natural resource   nonrenewable resource   recycling   pollutant
inexhaustible resource   fossil fuel   preservation   acid rain
renewable resource   conservation

C. Choose the correct vocabulary word to complete each sentence.

1. Because it can never be used up, sunlight is an __inexhaustible resource__ .

2. The process of ___recycling___ allows old plastic to be made into new plastic.

3. Lowering the heat in a building results in the ___conservation___ of fuel.

4. Decayed plants and animals from long ago can form a ___fossil fuel___

5. Because new trees can be planted, wood is a ___renewable resource___

6. A pollutant formed when factory smoke mixes with rain is ___acid rain___

7. Each of the following—water, natural gas, food, sunlight—is an example of a ___natural resource___ .

8. If a resource can be used up and cannot be replaced, it is a ___nonrenewable resource___

9. One way to practice ___preservation___ is to keep pollutants out of water.

10. Acid rain is a ___pollutant___ that can kill fish.

---

natural resource   nonrenewable resource   recycling   pollutant
inexhaustible resource   fossil fuel   preservation   acid rain
renewable resource   conservation

Students' answers will vary.

D. Use each pair of words in a sentence.

1. fossil fuel, nonrenewable resource
Because a fossil fuel began forming millions of years ago, it is a nonrenewable resource.

2. conservation, recycling
Since recycling uses old goods to make new ones, it may result in the conservation of a natural resource.

3. natural resource, preservation
Preservation of a natural resource is accomplished by not using the resource or by keeping the resource clean.

4. acid rain, pollutant
Acid rain is a pollutant that can kill fish and trees.

5. inexhaustible resource, renewable resource
Unlike a renewable resource, an inexhaustible resource never needs to be replaced.

Write!

Write your response to the prompt on a separate sheet of paper. Use as many vocabulary words as you can in your writing.

If you were in charge of protecting natural resources, what rules and laws would you make for different types of resources?

Write!

Distribute Writing Graphic Organizer: Main Idea and Details Chart, Teacher Guide page 80. Have students work with a partner or in a small group to brainstorm ideas for writing. Tell students to write a main idea about protecting natural resources in the Main Idea box and details of what they would do in the Details boxes.

Sample Answer

I would make strict new laws. I would support everyone who uses a natural resource that is an inexhaustible resource. I would pass a law making people practice preservation and conservation of every nonrenewable resource. This would include fossil fuel. I would require recycling. I would make a rule to renew every renewable resource before it is used up. I would make more laws against companies that add pollutants such as acid rain to the air, water, and soil.

TAKE-HOME ACTIVITY

Assign the Take-Home Activity to students for additional practice with the target vocabulary words. The reproducible Take-Home Activity for Lesson 8 is on page 91 of the Teacher Guide.

TAKE HOME 8

natural resource   nonrenewable resource   recycling   pollutant
inexhaustible resource   fossil fuel   preservation   acid rain
renewable resource   conservation

Use vocabulary words to complete the puzzle.

Protecting Earth's Resources

ACROSS

7 a resource, like the sun, that cannot be used up

8 a chemical from human activities that harms natural resources

9 protection of natural resources by using less of them

10 using materials from used goods to make new goods

DOWN

1 a resource that cannot be replaced

2 a resource that can be replaced

3 oil, coal, or natural gas

4 a pollutant made of acid from factory smoke in rain

5 something found in nature that people use

6 protection of natural resources by not using them

  Tell someone in your family what you have learned about protecting Earth's resources.

LESSON 9

Earth's Atmosphere

(Student Book pages 52–57)

TARGET VOCABULARY

atmosphere all the air surrounding Earth

troposphere the layer of atmosphere at Earth's surface

water vapor water in the form of gas

nitrogen the most common gas in air

oxygen the second most common gas in air

stratosphere the atmosphere layer above the troposphere

ozone layer the layer in the stratosphere where ozone is found

mesosphere the layer of atmosphere above the stratosphere

thermosphere the layer of atmosphere right above the mesosphere

exosphere the top layer of atmosphere

COGNATES

Spanish-speaking students may find a discussion of the similarities and differences between English and Spanish cognates helpful.

English	Spanish
atmosphere	atmósfera
troposphere	troposfera
vapor	vapor
nitrogen	nitrógeno
oxygen	oxígeno
stratosphere	estratosfera
ozone layer	capa de ozono

VOCABULARY STRATEGY: Roots

Explain that scientists have named the atmosphere and its layers using the root *sphere*. Ask students what a sphere is (*a globe, ball, round-shaped object, planet*). Ask why the root *sphere* helps to describe the air around Earth (*because of the round shape of Earth*). Have students list all the words from this lesson that include the root *sphere* (*atmosphere, troposphere, stratosphere, mesosphere, thermosphere, exosphere*). Discuss that the meaning of each of these words is made unique by the prefix added to the root. Encourage students to add these words to the root words chart on page 99 of their book.

Lesson Summary The atmosphere is the air that surrounds Earth. The atmosphere has five main layers based on temperature. Beginning at Earth's surface, the troposphere contains most of the water vapor and clouds. Air in the troposphere is about 78% nitrogen and 21% oxygen. The next layer, the stratosphere, contains the ozone layer that absorbs harmful rays of the sun. Above the stratosphere are the mesosphere, the thermosphere, and finally the widest layer reaching into space, the exosphere.

BEFORE READING

Activate Prior Knowledge

Show students a globe or picture of Earth and ask them what surrounds Earth (*air, the atmosphere*). Have them begin a three-column chart of what they know about the atmosphere ("I Know"), what they want to learn ("I Want to Learn"), and what they have learned ("What I Learned"). As they read the lesson, have them fill in what they learned.

Introduce Target Vocabulary

Tell students they are about to read a selection about Earth's atmosphere. Write the target vocabulary words on the board. Model the pronunciation of each word and have student volunteers repeat the word. Discuss the meaning of each word and, if necessary, write the definition next to the word.

Present Graphic Organizer

Provide each student with a copy of Vocabulary Graphic Organizer, Word Web, Teacher Guide page 76. Have students write *Earth's Atmosphere* in the center circle of the web. As they read the lesson, have students group related target vocabulary words in the outer circles. Have them write a phrase next to each circle that explains why they grouped the words together. Tell them they may add circles, if necessary.

Word and Definition Cards
for Lesson 9 are on pages 115 and 116
of the Teacher Guide.

Earth's Atmosphere

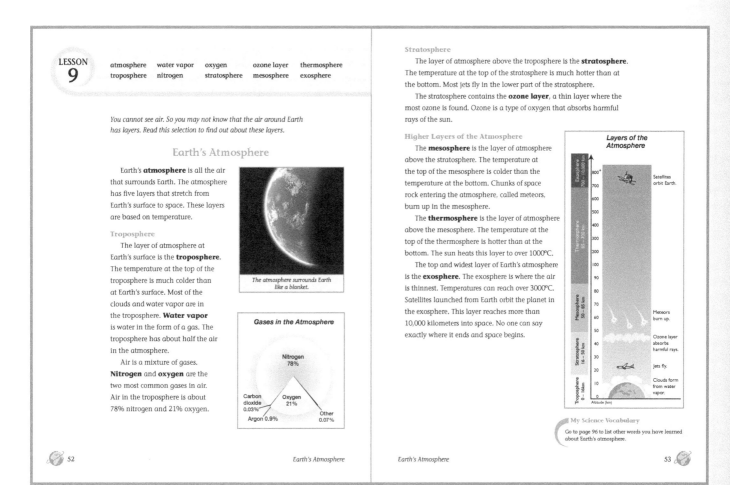

DURING READING

Read the selection aloud to students, stopping at the end of each paragraph or section. Review any words or concepts that students are having trouble with. Remind students that there is a glossary at the back of their book that contains all of the words that appear in boldfaced type in the lesson.

- Have students list the words that contain *sphere* and circle the prefixes. Tell students what each prefix means: *tropo-*, "turn or change"; *strato-*, "covering layer"; *meso-*, "middle"; *thermo-*, "heat"; *exo-*, "outside, beyond." Have them explain how each prefix relates to the meaning of the word that contains it (*troposphere—the layer where air turns and changes with weather; stratosphere—this layer covers the troposphere; mesosphere—the middle layer; thermosphere—this layer has high temperature; exosphere—the layer farthest out, beyond the other layers*).

- Ask students if they know about holes in the ozone layer in the stratosphere, which protects Earth from harmful radiation. Ask what might happen without the ozone layer. (*Harmful rays could reach Earth.*)

- Direct student's attention to the circle graph on page 52. Point out that nitrogen and oxygen together make up about 99% of the atmosphere. Other gases include almost 0.9% argon, 0.03% carbon dioxide, 0.07% all others. Explain that the percentage of water vapor in air varies because it is not part of the basic mixture.

Have students read the selection again on their own.

AFTER READING

Review Graphic Organizers
Answer any questions students have about the reading selection. Then have students complete or review their graphic organizer and share it with the class.

Summarize
Have students work together to come up with either a written or an oral summary of the lesson. Encourage students to use the target vocabulary words as the basis of their summary. Have students share their summary with the class.

My Science Vocabulary
Encourage students to turn to My Science Vocabulary on page 96 of the student book and use the space provided to add other words about Earth's atmosphere.

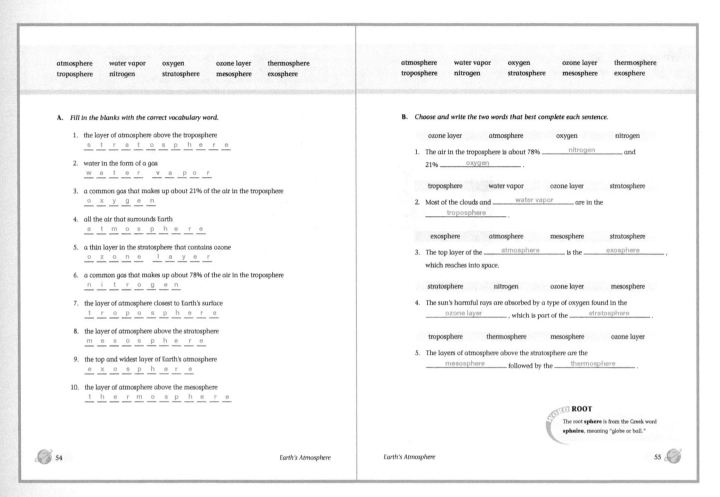

The worksheet pages shown contain:

Page 54:

atmosphere   water vapor   oxygen   ozone layer   thermosphere
troposphere   nitrogen   stratosphere   mesosphere   exosphere

A. *Fill in the blanks with the correct vocabulary word.*

1. the layer of atmosphere above the troposphere
   s t r a t o s p h e r e

2. water in the form of a gas
   w a t e r   v a p o r

3. a common gas that makes up about 21% of the air in the troposphere
   o x y g e n

4. all the air that surrounds Earth
   a t m o s p h e r e

5. a thin layer in the stratosphere that contains ozone
   o z o n e   l a y e r

6. a common gas that makes up about 78% of the air in the troposphere
   n i t r o g e n

7. the layer of atmosphere closest to Earth's surface
   t r o p o s p h e r e

8. the layer of atmosphere above the stratosphere
   m e s o s p h e r e

9. the top and widest layer of Earth's atmosphere
   e x o s p h e r e

10. the layer of atmosphere above the mesosphere
    t h e r m o s p h e r e

54   Earth's Atmosphere

Page 55:

atmosphere   water vapor   oxygen   ozone layer   thermosphere
troposphere   nitrogen   stratosphere   mesosphere   exosphere

B. *Choose and write the two words that best complete each sentence.*

ozone layer   atmosphere   oxygen   nitrogen

1. The air in the troposphere is about 78% ___nitrogen___ and
   21% ___oxygen___ .

troposphere   water vapor   ozone layer   stratosphere

2. Most of the clouds and ___water vapor___ are in the
   ___troposphere___ .

exosphere   atmosphere   mesosphere   stratosphere

3. The top layer of the ___atmosphere___ is the ___exosphere___ ,
   which reaches into space.

stratosphere   nitrogen   ozone layer   mesosphere

4. The sun's harmful rays are absorbed by a type of oxygen found in the
   ___ozone layer___ , which is part of the ___stratosphere___ .

troposphere   thermosphere   mesosphere   ozone layer

5. The layers of atmosphere above the stratosphere are the
   ___mesosphere___ followed by the ___thermosphere___ .

WORD ROOT

The root **sphere** is from the Greek word
sphaira, meaning "globe or ball."

Earth's Atmosphere   55

ACTIVITIES A–D

Encourage students to complete as many of the
activities as possible. Remind students that they
may refer to the Glossary at the back of their book
as they complete the activities. Students may work
independently, in small groups, or as a class. When
students are done, discuss the answers for each activity.

Extensions

These extension ideas allow you to reuse or expand
upon the activities. Share them with students who
complete the activities before other students, or have
students do them for additional practice with the
target vocabulary words.

A Draw a diagram of the layers of the atmosphere
and use the target vocabulary words as labels.

B Draw a circle around each target vocabulary word
that names a part of the atmosphere and underline
each vocabulary word that names something in the
atmosphere.

WORD ROOT

Tell students that the prefix *atmo-* comes from the
Greek word *atmos*, meaning "vapor or breath." Ask
them to explain how the parts work together in the
word *atmosphere*. (*It is the sphere, or ball, of vapor,
or air we breathe.*)

C Have students circle all the prepositional phrases
in the sentences. Have them tell what each
prepositional phrase adds; for example:
(*"of atmosphere" tells what layer; "above the
troposphere" tells where the layer is*). Remind
students to look for the prepositions *above, in,
with, between, of, from,* and *below.*

D Write a second sentence that could be logically
placed before or after each of the sentences.

atmosphere   water vapor   oxygen   ozone layer   thermosphere
troposphere   nitrogen   stratosphere   mesosphere   exosphere

C. *Choose the correct vocabulary word to complete each sentence.*

1. Water in the form of a gas is _____water vapor_____ .

2. Most clouds form in the bottom layer of the atmosphere, or
_____troposphere_____

3. The layer of atmosphere between the thermosphere and
the stratosphere is the _____mesosphere_____ .

4. The gas that makes up about 78% of the air in the troposphere
is _____nitrogen_____

5. Jets fly in the lower part of the _____stratosphere_____ , just above
the troposphere.

6. A thin layer with ozone gas, called the _____ozone layer_____ ,
helps protect Earth from harmful rays of the sun.

7. The layer of atmosphere farthest from Earth's surface is
the _____exosphere_____ .

8. All the layers of air stretching from Earth's surface to space make up
the _____atmosphere_____ .

9. The layer of atmosphere above the mesosphere and below
the exosphere is the _____thermosphere_____ .

10. About 21% of the air in the troposphere is the gas
_____oxygen_____ .

 56   *Earth's Atmosphere*

---

atmosphere   water vapor   oxygen   ozone layer   thermosphere
troposphere   nitrogen   stratosphere   mesosphere   exosphere

Students' answers will vary.

D. *Use each pair of words in a sentence.*

1. nitrogen, oxygen
The two most common gases in air are nitrogen and oxygen.

2. mesosphere, atmosphere
The mesosphere is the layer of atmosphere between the stratosphere
and the thermosphere.

3. water vapor, troposphere
Most of the atmosphere's water vapor is in the troposphere.

4. ozone layer, stratosphere
The ozone layer is a thin layer of ozone in the stratosphere.

5. exosphere, thermosphere
The top two layers of the atmosphere are the thermosphere
and then the exosphere.

 Write!

Write your response to the prompt on a separate sheet of paper.
Use as many vocabulary words as you can in your writing.

Imagine that you could see the layers of the atmosphere. What features and
changes would you observe if you traveled from Earth's surface to space?

Earth's Atmosphere   57

Write!

Distribute Writing Graphic Organizer: Sequence Chart,
Teacher Guide page 83. Tell students to write in the
first box of the chart the features and changes they
would observe as they start a trip in the troposphere.
In the following boxes, they should describe in order
what they would observe in each layer of the
atmosphere. They may add boxes, if necessary.

Sample Answer

   At the bottom of the atmosphere, the air is 78%
nitrogen and 21% oxygen. As I go up in the troposphere,
temperatures get cooler. I see clouds from water vapor in
the air. In the stratosphere, I see jets flying. I check out
the ozone layer. The temperature goes up until I reach the
mesosphere. Then it gets cooler. In the thermosphere,
temperatures really heat up. A meteor rushes past. Above,
in the exosphere, it's very hot. A satellite whizzes by me!

TAKE-HOME ACTIVITY

Assign the Take-Home Activity to students for
additional practice with the target vocabulary words.
The reproducible Take-Home Activity for Lesson 9
is on page 92 of the Teacher Guide.

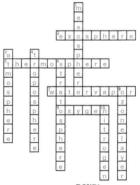

TAKE HOME 9

atmosphere   water vapor   oxygen   ozone layer   thermosphere
troposphere   nitrogen   stratosphere   mesosphere   exosphere

Use vocabulary words to complete the puzzle.

Earth's Atmosphere

ACROSS
2 the top and widest layer of the
atmosphere
5 the layer of atmosphere right above the
mesosphere
7 water in the form of a gas
9 a gas that makes up 21% of the
troposphere

DOWN
1 the layer of atmosphere above the
stratosphere
3 all the air surrounding Earth
4 the layer of atmosphere closest to
Earth's surface
6 the layer of atmosphere above the
troposphere
8 the layer in the stratosphere that
contains a type of oxygen that absorbs
harmful rays of the sun
10 a gas in air that makes up 78%
of the troposphere

 Tell someone in your family what you have learned about
Earth's atmosphere.

92   ©Curriculum Associates, LLC *Passwords: Science Vocabulary, Earth Science, Lesson 9*

Earth's Atmosphere   51

LESSON 10
Earth's Water Systems

(Student Book pages 58–63)

Lesson Summary The water cycle is the movement of Earth's water. Water on Earth's surface is heated by the sun and evaporates. As the water vapor rises, it cools and begins to condense. Eventually, it falls back to Earth as precipitation. At the surface, the water may flow over the ground as runoff or into a stream that is part of a river's watershed. Surface water may also become groundwater in an aquifer. The height of groundwater below the surface is the water table.

TARGET VOCABULARY

evaporation the change from liquid to gas

humidity the amount of water vapor in air

condensation the change from gas to liquid

precipitation water falling to Earth

surface water water at Earth's surface

runoff the water that flows on top of the land

watershed the area drained by a river

groundwater water under Earth's surface

aquifer an underground layer of rock filled with water

water table the height of groundwater under the ground

COGNATES

Spanish-speaking students may find a discussion of the similarities and differences between English and Spanish cognates helpful.

English	Spanish
evaporation	evaporación
humidity	humedad
condensation	condensación
precipitation	precipitación
surface	superficie
aquifer	acuífero

BEFORE READING

Activate Prior Knowledge

Have students brainstorm a list of all water sources and bodies of water on Earth. For each source, ask, "Where does this water come from?" Have students trace the water back as far as they can. Have students review their lists as they read the lesson.

Introduce Target Vocabulary

Tell students they are about to read a selection about Earth's water systems. Write the target vocabulary words on the board. Model the pronunciation of each word and have student volunteers repeat the word. Discuss the meaning of each word and, if necessary, write the definition next to the word.

Present Graphic Organizer

Provide each student with a copy of Vocabulary Graphic Organizer: Cycle, Teacher Guide page 79. On the line in the center of the organizer, have students write *The Water Cycle*. Tell them the top half of the circle represents above Earth's surface and the bottom half below. Have them add target vocabulary words inside along the circumference of the circle, in a logical order and placement, as they read the lesson.

> Word and Definition Cards
> for Lesson 10 are on pages 117 and 118
> of the Teacher Guide.

VOCABULARY STRATEGY: Using Known Words

Explain that sometimes to understand science terms students need only to use their knowledge of known words. Point out the term *surface water*. This term means what it seems to mean: *surface water* is "water at the surface." Have students define *groundwater* and *runoff*, using the known words.

(*Groundwater* is "water under the ground." *Runoff* is "water that runs off the ground.") Students may also point out that *water table* is "the tabletop of water under the surface" and *watershed* is "a region that sheds water to a single river."

Earth's Water Systems

evaporation condensation surface water watershed aquifer
humidity precipitation runoff groundwater water table

You can see water in rivers, streams, lakes, and oceans.
Read this selection to learn how water moves around Earth.

Earth's Water Systems

Water in the Air

Earth's water goes through a series of repeating steps called the water cycle. One step is **evaporation**, the changing from a liquid to a gas. Liquid water evaporates, forming water vapor, a gas. Evaporation requires heat. Most evaporation of water occurs when the sun heats the surface of the oceans. This is why **humidity**, or the amount of water vapor in the air, is high over the oceans.

As the water vapor rises from Earth's surface, it cools and changes back to a liquid. The changing from a gas to a liquid is **condensation**. Condensation is another step in the water cycle.

Over time, tiny droplets of water in the air gather to form clouds. Wind may move these clouds over land. The droplets may become so heavy that they fall back to Earth as rain, snow, sleet, or hail. Water falling to Earth as a liquid or solid is **precipitation**. Precipitation is another step in the water cycle.

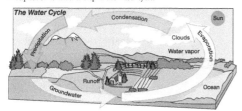

The Water Cycle — Condensation, Sun, Clouds, Water vapor, Evaporation, Precipitation, Runoff, Groundwater, Ocean

Water on the Ground

When precipitation reaches Earth's surface, it is called **surface water**. Most surface water is stored in oceans, lakes, rivers, and streams. Surface water that flows on top of the land is called **runoff**. Runoff collects in small streams that flow into a larger river. The area of land drained in this way is the river's **watershed**. The river water finally reaches the ocean, and the cycle continues.

Large Watershed Areas of the United States — Columbia River watershed, Mississippi River watershed, Colorado River watershed

Water Under the Ground

Precipitation may also sink into the ground. Water that is beneath Earth's surface is **groundwater**. Groundwater fills small spaces in soil. Also, some rocks have tiny spaces, or pores, that groundwater can fill. When a layer of rock with pores is sandwiched between rock that cannot absorb water, an aquifer forms. An **aquifer** is a layer of rock that fills with groundwater.

The height of groundwater under the ground is the **water table**. A high water table means that water is close to or at the surface, where it may form a pool or a lake. A low water table means that water is far below the surface. For example, a desert has a low water table.

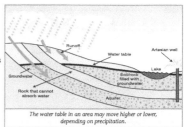

Runoff, Water table, Artesian well, Groundwater, Lake, Soil/rock filled with groundwater, Rock that cannot absorb water, Aquifer

The water table in an area may move higher or lower, depending on precipitation.

 My Science Vocabulary
Go to page 97 to list other words you have learned about Earth's water systems.

DURING READING

Read the selection aloud to students, stopping at the end of each paragraph or section. Review any words or concepts that students are having trouble with. Remind students that there is a glossary at the back of their book that contains all of the words that appear in boldfaced type in the lesson.

- Remind students that the suffix *-ion* can make a noun out of a verb. Have students tell the verb that goes with each target vocabulary word ending in *-ion. (evaporation—evaporate; condensation—condense; precipitation— precipitate).* Encourage students to add these words to the suffix chart on page 100 of their book.

- Refer students to the diagram on page 58. Ask students which labels name processes in the water cycle *(evaporation, condensation, precipitation),* which name sources and forms of water *(groundwater, runoff, ocean, water vapor, clouds),* and which names the driving force of the water cycle *(sun).*

- Point out that the following terms for water— *surface water, runoff, aquifer, groundwater,* and *water table*—all have to do with the location of the water. Have students tell where each is found.

Have students read the selection again on their own.

AFTER READING

Review Graphic Organizers

Answer any questions students have about the reading selection. Then have students complete or review their graphic organizer and share it with the class.

Summarize

Have students work together to come up with either a written or an oral summary of the lesson. Encourage students to use the target vocabulary words as the basis of their summary. Have students share their summary with the class.

My Science Vocabulary

Encourage students to turn to My Science Vocabulary on page 97 of the student book and use the space provided to add other words about Earth's water systems.

A. *Fill in the blanks with the correct vocabulary word.*

1. surface water that flows on top of the land
   r u n o f f

2. the changing from a gas to a liquid
   c o n d e n s a t i o n

3. the height of groundwater under the ground
   w a t e r   t a b l e

4. the area of land drained by a river and the streams that flow into the river
   w a t e r s h e d

5. rain, snow, sleet, or hail
   p r e c i p i t a t i o n

6. the changing from a liquid to a gas
   e v a p o r a t i o n

7. water that is beneath Earth's surface
   g r o u n d w a t e r

8. a layer of rock that fills with groundwater
   a q u i f e r

9. the amount of water vapor in the air
   h u m i d i t y

10. water on Earth's surface
    s u r f a c e   w a t e r

B. *Circle the word that makes sense in each sentence. Then write the word.*

1. Heat from the sun causes (evaporation, condensation) at the surface of the oceans. ___evaporation___

2. A lake forms where the (water table, condensation) is high enough to reach the surface. ___water table___

3. There is much higher (runoff, humidity) over oceans than over deserts. ___humidity___

4. Groundwater fills up pores in underground rock in an (evaporation, aquifer). ___aquifer___

5. Rain falling to Earth is a form of (groundwater, precipitation). ___precipitation___

6. When water vapor in the air cools, (watershed, condensation) occurs. ___condensation___

7. The area drained by the Mississippi River and its smaller streams is a huge (aquifer, watershed). ___watershed___

8. Where there is heavy rain and the land cannot absorb all the water, there will be much (runoff, groundwater). ___runoff___

9. An aquifer fills with (surface water, groundwater). ___groundwater___

10. When precipitation reaches Earth's surface, the water is called (evaporation, surface water). ___surface water___

ROOT
The word **aquifer** comes from the Latin **aqua**, which means "water."

ACTIVITIES A–D

Encourage students to complete as many of the activities as possible. Remind students that they may refer to the Glossary at the back of their book as they complete the activities. Students may work independently, in small groups, or as a class. When students are done, discuss the answers for each activity.

Extensions

These extension ideas allow you to reuse or expand upon the activities. Share them with students who complete the activities before other students, or have students do them for additional practice with the target vocabulary words.

A Circle all the nouns in the definitions of the target vocabulary words.

B Choose one sentence and draw a diagram that would help someone understand the concept.

WORD ROOT

Ask students to use the meaning of the root *aqua* to define *aquifer (an underground layer of rock filled with water)*. Have students use what they know about *aqua* to guess the definitions of one or more of the following words: *aquatic, aquaculture, aquanaut, aquarium.* Encourage students to add these words to the root words chart on page 99 of their book.

C For each completed sentence, write a question that would be answered by the sentence.

D Write *S* next to each simple sentence. (A simple sentence has one subject and one verb.) Write *NS* next to each sentence that is not a simple sentence.

C. *Write the vocabulary word that best completes each pair of sentences.*

1. Rain, sleet, hail, and snow are ___precipitation___ .
   Water falling to Earth is ___precipitation___ .

2. A layer of rock with pores fills with water and creates an ___aquifer___ .
   An ___aquifer___ is sandwiched between rock that cannot absorb water.

3. The height of groundwater is the ___water table___ .
   In the desert, the ___water table___ is low.

4. The process of ___condensation___ occurs when water vapor cools.
   The changing of water vapor to liquid water is ___condensation___ .

5. The amount of water vapor in the air is ___humidity___ .
   Over the oceans, the ___humidity___ of the air is high.

6. When precipitation reaches Earth's surface, the water is called ___surface water___ .
   Runoff is ___surface water___ that flows over land.

7. Water that sinks into the ground is ___groundwater___ .
   Spaces in rocks and soil fill with ___groundwater___ .

8. The changing from liquid to water vapor is ___evaporation___ .
   Heat from the sun causes the ___evaporation___ of liquid water.

9. The land drained by a river and its streams is the river's ___watershed___ .
   A river and its streams collect runoff to form the river's ___watershed___ .

10. Water running on top of the land is ___runoff___ .
    Small streams carry ___runoff___ to a larger river.

Students' answers will vary.

D. *Use each word in a sentence that shows you understand the meaning of the word.*

1. aquifer ___An aquifer holds groundwater.___

2. groundwater ___Groundwater flows underground.___

3. water table ___A low water table means groundwater is far below the surface.___

4. evaporation ___A wet towel can dry by evaporation.___

5. humidity ___When humidity is high, the air feels damp.___

6. condensation ___Condensation is the step in the water cycle when water vapor changes to liquid water.___

7. precipitation ___Water can fall to Earth as a liquid or a solid form of precipitation.___

8. watershed ___A large river carries the water from its watershed to the ocean.___

9. surface water ___Most surface water becomes runoff.___

10. runoff ___Runoff occurs where precipitation cannot sink into the ground.___

Write!

Write your response to the prompt on a separate sheet of paper. Use as many vocabulary words as you can in your writing.

If you could follow one drop of water as it goes through the water cycle, what events in the life of this drop of water would you witness?

Write!

Distribute Writing Graphic Organizer: Narrative Map, Teacher Guide page 82. Have students work with a partner or in a small group to brainstorm ideas for writing. They may be the main character, or make a drop of water the main character. Setting(s) will include all the places the drop travels. Main events will include what will occur.

Sample Answer

The air has much water vapor. I'm a single drop of that humidity. Evaporation removes me from the ocean's surface. High in the air, condensation changes me back to a liquid. Soon, I gather with friends, and we fall as rain. So much happens to us all as surface water. Some of my friends are runoff, flowing into a small stream and then a river with a huge watershed. Some fall into a lake whose surface is the water table. I sink into the ground to become groundwater in an aquifer.

TAKE-HOME ACTIVITY

Assign the Take-Home Activity to students for additional practice with the target vocabulary words. The reproducible Take-Home Activity for Lesson 10 is on page 93 of the Teacher Guide.

Earth's Water Systems

TAKE HOME **10**

Use vocabulary words to complete the puzzle.

Earth's Water Systems

ACROSS

2. the change from a gas to a liquid
6. water falling to Earth as a liquid or a solid
7. the height of water under the ground
8. an underground layer of rock filled with groundwater
9. precipitation that has reached Earth's surface
10. water that flows on top of the land

DOWN

1. water that is beneath Earth's surface
3. the change from a liquid to a gas
4. the amount of water vapor in the air
5. the land area drained by a river

 Tell someone in your family what you have learned about Earth's water systems.

    93

LESSON 11

The Ocean Floor

(Student Book pages 64–69)

TARGET VOCABULARY

ocean floor the land under the oceans

continental shelf the underwater land at the edge of a continent

continental slope the steeply sloped ocean floor beyond the continental shelf

submarine canyon an underwater valley

continental rise the ocean floor beyond the continental slope

abyssal plain the fairly level, deep ocean floor

seamount an underwater volcanic mountain

oceanic ridge a long range of mountains on the ocean floor

trench a very deep, wide valley on the ocean floor

subduction zone an area where one plate of ocean floor is sliding under another

COGNATES

Spanish-speaking students may find a discussion of the similarities and differences between English and Spanish cognates helpful.

English	Spanish
ocean	océano
continental shelf	plataforma continental
submarine	submarino
abyssal plain	planicie abisal
subduction zone	zona de subducción

Lesson Summary The ocean floor has specific features from the edges of continents to the mid-ocean ridges. Underwater land at the edge of a continent is the continental shelf. From there, the continental slope with submarine canyons and the continental rise lead to the deep-ocean abyssal plain, which extends to the mid-ocean ridge. Isolated volcanoes called seamounts dot the abyssal plain. Deep trenches form where one plate of oceanic crust slips under another at a subduction zone.

BEFORE READING

Activate Prior Knowledge

Have students read the introductory paragraph on page 64. Then have them draw a sketch of what they think the land looks like underwater. Have students show and discuss their sketches.

Introduce Target Vocabulary

Tell students they are about to read a selection about the ocean floor. Write the target vocabulary words on the board. Model the pronunciation of each word and have student volunteers repeat the word. Discuss the meaning of each word and, if necessary, write the definition next to the word.

Present Graphic Organizer

Provide each student with a copy of Vocabulary Graphic Organizer, Word Web, Teacher Guide page 76. Have students write *Ocean Floor* in the center circle of the web. As they read the lesson, have students group related target vocabulary words in the outer circles. Have them write a phrase next to each circle that explains why they grouped the words together. Tell them they may add circles, if necessary.

Word and Definition Cards
for Lesson 11 are on pages 119 and 120
of the Teacher Guide.

VOCABULARY STRATEGY: Prefix

Remind students that a prefix is a word part added at the beginning of a word. A prefix affects the meaning of a word or root. Have students find the target vocabulary word *submarine canyon* and separate *submarine* into its prefix and root (*sub-, marine*). Tell students that the prefix *sub-* means "under" and *marine* means "water." Have them explain the meaning of the term (*a canyon under water*). Have students find the other vocabulary word that uses the prefix *sub-* (*subduction*). Explain that *duct* means "to lead or draw." Ask students what a *subduction zone* is (*area where one plate is drawn under another*). Challenge students to think of other words that use the prefix *sub-* as "under" (*subway, subsoil, submerge, suboceanic, subsolar, subscript*).

The Ocean Floor

ocean floor submarine canyon seamount trench
continental shelf continental rise oceanic ridge subduction zone
continental slope abyssal plain

The land you see has mountains, valleys, hills, and plains. What about the land under the ocean? Is it smooth and level, or as varied as the land you see? Read this selection to see if you guessed correctly.

The Ocean Floor

From the Shore to the Depths

Under the oceans, the land is called the **ocean floor**. The ocean floor changes from the shore of the continents to the deep ocean

Land at the edge of a continent gently slopes underwater and is called the **continental shelf**. The continental shelf is really part of Earth's crust that makes up the continents, even though it's underwater.

At the edge of the continental shelf, the ocean floor drops sharply downward as the **continental slope**. This slope is still part of the continental crust. On the continental slope, V-shaped valleys form. A deep underwater valley with sharp sides is a **submarine canyon**. Submarine canyons carry water and bits of rock from land toward the deep ocean floor.

Stretching between the continental slope and the deep ocean floor is the **continental rise**. The continental rise is less steep than the continental slope. The continental rise is covered with bits of rock from the land.

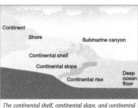
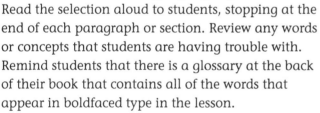

The continental shelf, continental slope, and continental rise all slope down to the deep ocean floor.

 64

The Ocean Floor

The Deep Ocean Floor

The continental rise slopes down to the abyssal plain. The **abyssal plain** is the fairly level ocean floor that stretches to the middle of the ocean. Over time, bits of rock have washed down from the continents to cover the abyssal plain.

Volcanoes erupt on the abyssal plain, but they are far apart. A volcanic mountain that forms on the ocean floor is a **seamount**. A seamount may grow large enough to reach the ocean's surface and become an island.

Each major ocean has a long chain of mountains, or an **oceanic ridge**, near its center. At a ridge, plates, or sections of Earth's crust, are moving apart. New land forms from molten rock flowing up through openings in the crust on the ocean floor. The rock comes from Earth's middle layer, the mantle.

New crust forms at the ridges, but old crust is lost at trenches. A **trench** is a very deep, wide valley that forms at a subduction zone. A **subduction zone** is an area where one plate of the ocean floor is sliding under another plate. At a trench, old crust returns to the mantle.

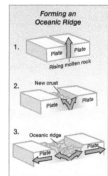

Forming an Oceanic Ridge

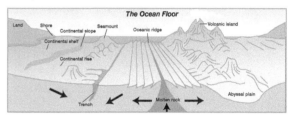

The Ocean Floor

My Science Vocabulary
Go to page 97 to list other words you have learned about the ocean floor.

The Ocean Floor

65

DURING READING

Read the selection aloud to students, stopping at the end of each paragraph or section. Review any words or concepts that students are having trouble with. Remind students that there is a glossary at the back of their book that contains all of the words that appear in boldfaced type in the lesson.

- Point out that *submarine*, besides being an adjective, is a noun naming a kind of ship. Have students explain why that is a good name *(the ship moves underwater)*.

- Have students find the three terms that use *continental* in the diagram on page 64. Explain that the adjective *continental* makes clear that the land so named—continental shelf, continental slope, and continental rise—is made up of continental crust underwater, rather than oceanic crust. So, the ocean floor has both continental and oceanic crust.

- Point out that *sea* is a synonym for *ocean*. Have students separate *seamount* into two words *(sea, mount)*. Have them explain how these words create the meaning given in the selection *(a volcanic mountain under the sea)*. Ask students to define the

similar compound term *oceanic ridge* *(a ridge under the ocean)*.

- Note that a trench is any kind of deep ditch. Tell students that the ocean trenches are the deepest parts of the ocean.

Have students read the selection again on their own.

AFTER READING

Review Graphic Organizers

Answer any questions students have about the reading selection. Then have students complete or review their graphic organizer and share it with the class.

Summarize

Have students work together to come up with either a written or an oral summary of the lesson. Encourage students to use the target vocabulary words as the basis of their summary. Have students share their summary with the class.

My Science Vocabulary

Encourage students to turn to My Science Vocabulary on page 97 of the student book and use the space provided to add other words about the ocean floor.

The Ocean Floor

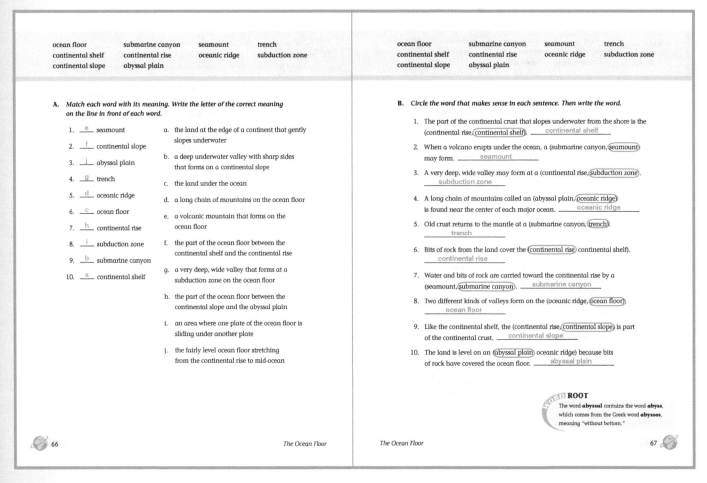

ocean floor submarine canyon seamount trench
continental shelf continental rise oceanic ridge subduction zone
continental slope abyssal plain

A. Match each word with its meaning. Write the letter of the correct meaning on the line in front of each word.

1. _e_ seamount
2. _f_ continental slope
3. _j_ abyssal plain
4. _g_ trench
5. _d_ oceanic ridge
6. _c_ ocean floor
7. _h_ continental rise
8. _i_ subduction zone
9. _b_ submarine canyon
10. _a_ continental shelf

a. the land at the edge of a continent that gently slopes underwater
b. a deep underwater valley with sharp sides that forms on a continental slope
c. the land under the ocean
d. a long chain of mountains on the ocean floor
e. a volcanic mountain that forms on the ocean floor
f. the part of the ocean floor between the continental shelf and the continental rise
g. a very deep, wide valley that forms at a subduction zone on the ocean floor
h. the part of the ocean floor between the continental slope and the abyssal plain
i. an area where one plate of the ocean floor is sliding under another plate
j. the fairly level ocean floor stretching from the continental rise to mid-ocean

ocean floor submarine canyon seamount trench
continental shelf continental rise oceanic ridge subduction zone
continental slope abyssal plain

B. Circle the word that makes sense in each sentence. Then write the word.

1. The part of the continental crust that slopes underwater from the shore is the (continental rise, (continental shelf)). _continental shelf_

2. When a volcano erupts under the ocean, a (submarine canyon, (seamount)) may form. _seamount_

3. A very deep, wide valley may form at a (continental rise, (subduction zone)). _subduction zone_

4. A long chain of mountains called an (abyssal plain, (oceanic ridge)) is found near the center of each major ocean. _oceanic ridge_

5. Old crust returns to the mantle at a (submarine canyon, (trench)). _trench_

6. Bits of rock from the land cover the ((continental rise) continental shelf). _continental rise_

7. Water and bits of rock are carried toward the continental rise by a (seamount, (submarine canyon)). _submarine canyon_

8. Two different kinds of valleys form on the (oceanic ridge, (ocean floor)). _ocean floor_

9. Like the continental shelf, the (continental rise, (continental slope)) is part of the continental crust. _continental slope_

10. The land is level on an ((abyssal plain) oceanic ridge) because bits of rock have covered the ocean floor. _abyssal plain_

ROOT
The word **abyssal** contains the word **abyss**, which comes from the Greek word **abyssos**, meaning "without bottom."

ACTIVITIES A–D

Encourage students to complete as many of the activities as possible. Remind students that they may refer to the Glossary at the back of their book as they complete the activities. Students may work independently, in small groups, or as a class. When students are done, discuss the answers for each activity.

Extensions

These extension ideas allow you to reuse or expand upon the activities. Share them with students who complete the activities before other students, or have students do them for additional practice with the target vocabulary words.

A Use the Internet or another source to find a diagram or photo of the ocean or the ocean floor. Write a caption that includes at least one target vocabulary word.

B Organize the target vocabulary words alphabetically under the heads *Words Beginning with A–G*, *Words Beginning with H–P*, and *Words Beginning with Q–Z*.

WORD ROOT

Have students explain why *abyssal* is a good adjective for the *abyssal plain*. (*This plain forms the base of the deep ocean floor.*)

C Select two or more categories in which to group the target vocabulary words, such as *Parts of the Ocean Floor, Ocean Features, etc.*

D Write another sentence for each pair of target vocabulary words using the opposite order of the vocabulary words from the first sentence.

ocean floor   submarine canyon   seamount   trench
continental shelf   continental rise   oceanic ridge   subduction zone
continental slope   abyssal plain

C. *Choose the correct vocabulary word to complete each sentence.*

1. A small volcanic island in the ocean may be the top of a _____ seamount _____.

2. As plates on the ocean floor move apart, molten rock from the mantle flows up through the opening and forms an _____ oceanic ridge _____.

3. At a subduction zone, a _____ trench _____ can form.

4. Bits of rock wash down from the continents, covering the _____ abyssal plain _____ and making it fairly level.

5. Between a continent's edge and the continental slope is the _____ continental shelf _____.

6. Some parts of the _____ ocean floor _____ are steep, and some parts are fairly level.

7. Between the continental shelf and the continental rise lies the _____ continental slope _____.

8. The sliding of one plate of the ocean floor under another plate creates a _____ subduction zone _____.

9. Like a trench, a _____ submarine canyon _____ is a deep underwater valley.

10. The part of the ocean floor between the continental slope and the abyssal plain is the _____ continental rise _____.

The Ocean Floor

---

ocean floor   submarine canyon   seamount   trench
continental shelf   continental rise   oceanic ridge   subduction zone
continental slope   abyssal plain

Students' answers will vary.
D. *Use each pair of words in a sentence.*

1. continental slope, submarine canyon
A submarine canyon on the continental slope carries bits of rock from land toward the deep ocean floor.

2. subduction zone, trench
A trench forms on the deep ocean floor at a subduction zone.

3. ocean floor, abyssal plain
On the deep ocean floor, the level abyssal plain has been filled in with bits of rock.

4. continental shelf, continental rise
The continental shelf is on one side of the continental slope, and the continental rise is on the other side.

5. seamount, oceanic ridge
A seamount is a single mountain, but an oceanic ridge is a chain of mountains.

 Write! _____
Write your response to the prompt on a separate sheet of paper. Use as many vocabulary words as you can in your writing.

If you could travel in an underwater ship from the shores of a continent to the deep ocean floor, what would you see?

The Ocean Floor

Write!

Distribute Writing Graphic Organizer: Sequence Chart, Teacher Guide page 83. Tell students to write in the first box of the chart what they would see at the start of a journey, at the shores of a continent. In the following boxes, they should write in order what they would see between the shores and mid-ocean and what they would see from mid-ocean to beyond.

Sample Answer

   On the ocean floor, I would cross the gently sloping continental shelf until I reached the sharply sloping continental slope. There, I would see a submarine canyon carrying bits of rock onto the continental rise and the abyssal plain. On the abyssal plain, I would find a seamount. In mid-ocean, I would find an oceanic ridge on either side of a valley. Finally, near the far coast, I might find a subduction zone with a very deep trench.

TAKE-HOME ACTIVITY

Assign the Take-Home Activity to students for additional practice with the target vocabulary words. The reproducible Take-Home Activity for Lesson 11 is on page 94 of the Teacher Guide.

TAKE HOME 11

ocean floor   submarine canyon   seamount   trench
continental shelf   continental rise   oceanic ridge   subduction zone
continental slope   abyssal plain

Use vocabulary words to complete the puzzle.

The Ocean Floor

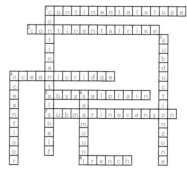

ACROSS

1 the ocean floor between the continental shelf and continental rise

2 the part of the ocean floor between the continental slope and the abyssal plain

4 a long chain of mountains on the ocean floor

5 the fairly level deep-ocean floor

7 a deep underwater valley on the continental slope

8 a very deep, wide valley that forms on the ocean floor

DOWN

1 the underwater land at the edge of a continent

3 an area where one plate of the ocean floor is sliding under another

4 the land under the oceans

6 an underwater volcanic mountain

 Tell someone in your family what you have learned about the ocean floor.

©Curriculum Associates, LLC *Passwords: Science Vocabulary, Earth Science, Lesson 11*

The Ocean Floor

LESSON 12

Earth's Changing Weather

(Student Book pages 70–75)

Lesson Summary Weather—the day-to-day changes that make up climate—is affected by moving air masses. An approaching warm front usually brings cirrus clouds and then stratus clouds with rain. An approaching cold front causes cumulus clouds to form. Winds blow from areas of high pressure to low pressure at Earth's surface. Above the surface are wind belts such as the westerlies and trade winds. Even higher, a narrow jet stream blows west to east over North America.

TARGET VOCABULARY

climate the average weather of a region

air mass a huge body of air with the same features

front where the edge of two air masses meet

cirrus clouds high, thin, icy clouds

stratus clouds low, gray clouds

cumulus clouds puffy, white clouds

air pressure the force of air pushing down on Earth

westerlies large belts of winds

trade winds the two large belts of winds near the equator

jet stream a narrow band of very strong winds high above Earth's surface

COGNATES

Spanish-speaking students may find a discussion of the similarities and differences between English and Spanish cognates helpful.

English	Spanish
climate	clima
air mass	masa de aire
front	frente
stratus	estrato
pressure	presión

BEFORE READING

Activate Prior Knowledge

Ask students to describe in as much detail as possible the weather today. Have them write the words they use on the board. Then have them imagine a day they have experienced when the weather was very different. For the different day, have them write words that describe ways it was different. Tell students that in this lesson, they will learn how weather changes.

Introduce Target Vocabulary

Tell students they are about to read a selection about Earth's changing weather. Write the target vocabulary words on the board. Model the pronunciation of each word and have student volunteers repeat the word. Discuss the meaning of each word and, if necessary, write the definition next to the word.

Present Graphic Organizer

Provide each student with a copy of Vocabulary Graphic Organizer: Four Square, Teacher Guide page 78. Assign each student one target vocabulary word to write in the center. Have students label the boxes: *Definition, Description, Location,* and *Example Picture/ Diagram.* As students read the lesson, have them add information to the boxes.

Word and Definition Cards
for Lesson 12 are on pages 121 and 122
of the Teacher Guide.

VOCABULARY STRATEGY: Context Clues

Remind students that context clues help readers understand unfamiliar words. Tell them that science writers often provide context clues that are the definition of an unfamiliar word. In this book, these direct-definition context clues are easy to spot because they often come after the boldfaced word and use a form of the verb *to be*. For an example,

read the first sentence aloud, "**Climate** is the average weather of a region over a long period of time." Explain that *climate* is the target vocabulary word and the definition is *"average weather of a region over a long period of time."* Have students underline the other direct-definition context clues that they find in this lesson.

Earth's Changing Weather

climate   front   stratus clouds   air pressure   trade winds
air mass   cirrus clouds cumulus clouds   westerlies   jet stream

Some days are hot and sunny, but others are cool and cloudy. Why does the weather change? What are some signs of changing weather? Read this selection to help you predict the weather.

Earth's Changing Weather

Climate is the average weather of a region over a long period of time. Weather is what is going on in the air at a given place and time. Weather changes when a new air mass moves over an area. An **air mass** is a huge body of air with the same features throughout, such as temperature and moisture.

A **front** is where the edges of two air masses meet. The approaching front is the leading edge of the air mass that is moving into the region where the other air mass already is. This approaching front brings weather changes.

Warm Fronts

A warm front is formed when a warm air mass moves toward a cold air mass. The air is heavier in a cold air mass than it is in a warm air mass. The lighter warm air rises slowly above the cold air. The first clouds to form are wispy cirrus clouds. **Cirrus clouds** are high, thin, icy clouds. Next, stratus clouds form. **Stratus clouds** are layers of low gray clouds that often bring steady rain.

Approaching Warm Front — Cirrus clouds, Warm air, Stratus clouds, Rain, Warm front, Cold air

Cold Fronts

A cold front is formed when a heavier cold air mass moves toward a warm air mass. The heavier cold air pushes the warm air upward suddenly. Large cumulus clouds form. **Cumulus clouds** are puffy white clouds that form low in the air to mid-height. Some cumulus clouds become thunderclouds with winds and rain.

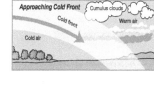

Approaching Cold Front — Cumulus clouds, Cold front, Warm air, Cold air

Winds

Air pressure is the force of air pushing down on Earth. Differences in air pressure cause local winds. Warm air has less air pressure than cold air. At Earth's surface, winds blow from areas of high pressure to areas of low pressure.

Above the surface, Earth has six large belts of wind. The winds in each belt blow in the same direction. Most of North America is in one of the two wind belts called the **westerlies**. The westerlies blow from west to east. Two wind belts called the **trade winds** are above and below the equator. Trade winds mostly blow from east to west.

Winds also blow high above Earth's surface in a **jet stream**, a narrow band with very strong winds that blow from west to east. One jet stream flows over North America.

Earth's six wind belts are caused by currents of air above Earth's surface.

Winter jet stream
Summer jet stream

The position of the jet stream over North America changes with the seasons.

My Science Vocabulary
Go to page 97 to list other words you have learned about Earth's changing weather.

DURING READING

Read the selection aloud to students, stopping at the end of each paragraph or section. Review any words or concepts that students are having trouble with. Remind students that there is a glossary at the back of their book that contains all of the words that appear in boldfaced type in the lesson.

- Have students draw or find on the Internet pictures of clouds and label them: *cirrus clouds, stratus clouds, cumulus clouds.*

- From a newspaper weather map or other source, have students copy the symbols for warm front and cold front. Have them explain what the symbols represent *(the leading edge of the air mass that is warm or cold).*

- Have students use a dictionary to find how westerlies got their name. *(Westerlies blow generally from the west.)* Explain that trade winds were named when sailing ships caught these regular winds to follow trade routes.

Have students read the selection again on their own.

AFTER READING

Review Graphic Organizers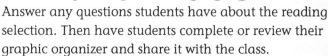

Answer any questions students have about the reading selection. Then have students complete or review their graphic organizer and share it with the class.

Summarize

Have students work together to come up with either a written or an oral summary of the lesson. Encourage students to use the target vocabulary words as the basis of their summary. Have students share their summary with the class.

My Science Vocabulary

Encourage students to turn to My Science Vocabulary on page 97 of the student book and use the space provided to add other words about Earth's changing weather.

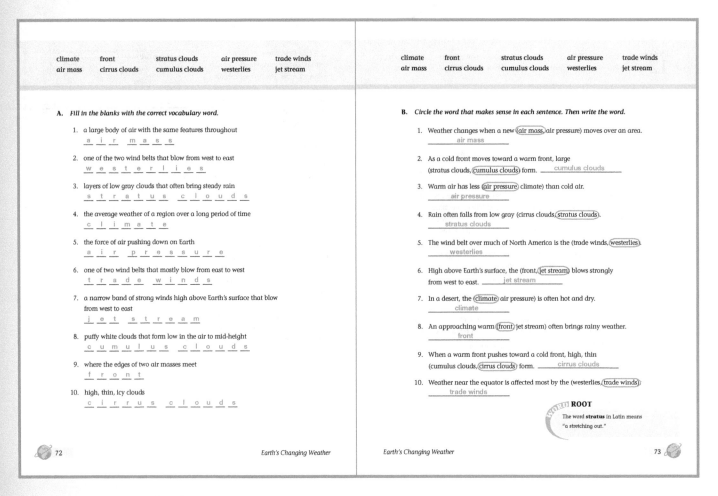

A. *Fill in the blanks with the correct vocabulary word.*

1. a large body of air with the same features throughout
   a i r   m a s s

2. one of the two wind belts that blow from west to east
   w e s t e r l i e s

3. layers of low gray clouds that often bring steady rain
   s t r a t u s   c l o u d s

4. the average weather of a region over a long period of time
   c l i m a t e

5. the force of air pushing down on Earth
   a i r   p r e s s u r e

6. one of two wind belts that mostly blow from east to west
   t r a d e   w i n d s

7. a narrow band of strong winds high above Earth's surface that blow from west to east
   j e t   s t r e a m

8. puffy white clouds that form low in the air to mid-height
   c u m u l u s   c l o u d s

9. where the edges of two air masses meet
   f r o n t

10. high, thin, icy clouds
    c i r r u s   c l o u d s

B. *Circle the word that makes sense in each sentence. Then write the word.*

1. Weather changes when a new (air mass, air pressure) moves over an area.
   air mass

2. As a cold front moves toward a warm front, large (stratus clouds, cumulus clouds) form. cumulus clouds

3. Warm air has less (air pressure, climate) than cold air.
   air pressure

4. Rain often falls from low gray (cirrus clouds, stratus clouds).
   stratus clouds

5. The wind belt over much of North America is the (trade winds, westerlies).
   westerlies

6. High above Earth's surface, the (front, jet stream) blows strongly from west to east. jet stream

7. In a desert, the (climate, air pressure) is often hot and dry.
   climate

8. An approaching warm (front, jet stream) often brings rainy weather.
   front

9. When a warm front pushes toward a cold front, high, thin (cumulus clouds, cirrus clouds) form. cirrus clouds

10. Weather near the equator is affected most by the (westerlies, trade winds).
    trade winds

ROOT
The word **stratus** in Latin means "a stretching out."

ACTIVITIES A–D

Encourage students to complete as many of the activities as possible. Remind students that they may refer to the Glossary at the back of their book as they complete the activities. Students may work independently, in small groups, or as a class. When students are done, discuss the answers for each activity.

Extensions

These extension ideas allow you to reuse or expand upon the activities. Share them with students who complete the activities before other students, or have students do them for additional practice with the target vocabulary words.

A Look for and share the multiple meanings of target vocabulary words and parts of compound vocabulary words, such as *jet* and *stream*.

B Circle the adjectives and underline the adverbs in the sentences.

WORD ROOT

Tell students that in Latin, *cirrus* means "curl or tuft" and *cumulus* means "heap." Discuss how the meaning of the words *stratus*, *cirrus*, and *cumulus* reflect the appearance of these clouds.

C Draw a picture illustrating one of the sentences.

D Choose one sentence and add at least two more sentences that add information about the topic or the target vocabulary word.

climate   front   stratus clouds   air pressure   trade winds
air mass   cirrus clouds   cumulus clouds   westerlies   jet stream

C. *Choose the correct vocabulary word to complete each sentence.*

1. The high, thin clouds that appear first when a warm front approaches are _____cirrus clouds_____

2. Differences in _____air pressure_____ cause local winds.

3. Above and below the equator, the _____trade winds_____ mostly blow from east to west.

4. After cirrus clouds form, layers of low _____stratus clouds_____ normally appear next.

5. The type of weather a region usually has is its _____climate_____.

6. When two air masses meet at a _____front_____, the weather usually changes.

7. In North America, the belt of wind that blows from west to east is the _____westerlies_____.

8. Some large, puffy _____cumulus clouds_____ may become thunderclouds.

9. The narrow band of strong winds blowing west to east high above North America is the _____jet stream_____.

10. A huge body of air with the same temperature, air pressure, and moisture throughout is an _____air mass_____.

 74

Earth's Changing Weather

---

climate   front   stratus clouds   air pressure   trade winds
air mass   cirrus clouds   cumulus clouds   westerlies   jet stream

Students' answers will vary.

D. *Use each word in a sentence that shows you understand the meaning of the word.*

1. cumulus clouds ___Thunderclouds are cumulus clouds.___

2. air mass ___An air mass can be warm or cold.___

3. westerlies ___Over North America, the westerlies blow from west to east.___

4. stratus clouds ___Stratus clouds bring rain.___

5. climate ___The climate at the North Pole is very cold.___

6. air pressure ___Warm air has less air pressure than cold air.___

7. jet stream ___The jet stream is the narrow band of winds blowing west to east high over North America.___

8. front ___When a warm front approaches a cold front, two kinds of clouds form.___

9. cirrus clouds ___Cirrus clouds arrive first with a warm front.___

10. trade winds ___Above and below the equator there are wind belts called trade winds.___

Write!

Write your response to the prompt on a separate sheet of paper. Use as many vocabulary words as you can in your writing.

If you could travel far above Earth, watching the winds and weather, what would you see?

Earth's Changing Weather   75

Write!

Distribute Writing Graphic Organizer: Idea Wheel, Teacher Guide page 81. Tell students to write *Winds and Weather* in the center of the wheel. Then on the spokes of the wheel, they should list/describe things they would see from far above Earth. Tell students they may add spokes to the wheel, if necessary.

Sample Answer

Looking down, I see how the climate changes. I also see patterns of winds. High above Earth, the jet stream rushes by. Below it, belts of winds, including westerlies and trade winds, cover the planet. I see high, wispy cirrus clouds and low, rainy stratus clouds over a place where a cold front is moving in. Winds are blowing from the cold air mass toward the warm air because of air pressure. Over here, puffy cumulus clouds mean a warm front is moving in.

TAKE-HOME ACTIVITY

Assign the Take-Home Activity to students for additional practice with the target vocabulary words. The reproducible Take-Home Activity for Lesson 12 is on page 95 of the Teacher Guide.

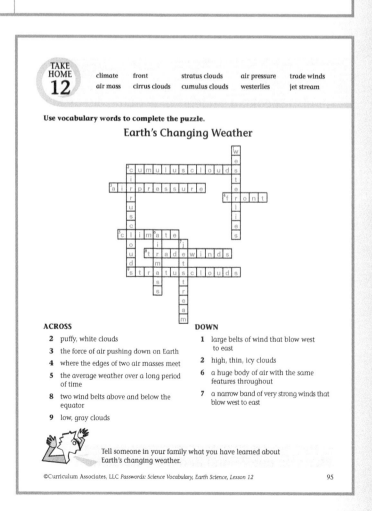

TAKE HOME 12

climate   front   stratus clouds   air pressure   trade winds
air mass   cirrus clouds   cumulus clouds   westerlies   jet stream

Use vocabulary words to complete the puzzle.

Earth's Changing Weather

ACROSS
2 puffy, white clouds
3 the force of air pushing down on Earth
4 where the edges of two air masses meet
5 the average weather over a long period of time
8 two wind belts above and below the equator
9 low, gray clouds

DOWN
1 large belts of wind that blow west to east
2 high, thin, icy clouds
6 a huge body of air with the same features throughout
7 a narrow band of very strong winds that blow west to east

Tell someone in your family what you have learned about Earth's changing weather.

©Curriculum Associates, LLC *Passwords: Science Vocabulary, Earth Science, Lesson 12*   95

Earth's Changing Weather

LESSON 13

Our Solar System and Beyond

(Student Book pages 76–81)

Lesson Summary Held together by gravity, the solar system includes the sun, the planets, and all other objects that orbit the sun, including natural satellites, asteroids, and comets. The planets include the rocky inner planets that orbit closer to the sun and the outer planets. Our sun is one of hundreds of billions of stars in the Milky Way galaxy. Scientists use the light-year to measure some distances in space. The universe, all the matter and energy that exists, contains billions of galaxies.

TARGET VOCABULARY

solar system the sun and all the objects that move around it

gravity the force of attraction between objects

inner planets the planets closest to the sun

satellite an object that moves around a larger object, a moon

outer planets the planets farther from the sun

asteroid a small, solid object of rock and metal orbiting the sun

comet a ball of rock, dust, and ice orbiting the sun

galaxy a large group of stars, planets, asteroids, moons, and comets held together by gravity

light-year the distance light travels in a year

universe all the matter and energy that exists

COGNATES

Spanish-speaking students may find a discussion of the similarities and differences between English and Spanish cognates helpful.

English	Spanish
solar system	sistema solar
gravity	gravedad
inner planets	planetas interiores
satellite	satélite
outer planets	planetas exteriores
asteroid	asteroide
comet	cometa
galaxy	galaxia
universe	universo

BEFORE READING

Activate Prior Knowledge

Ask students to name as many planets as they can and write the names on the board. Ask students to tell ways these planets are alike and ways they are different. Tell students that in this lesson, they will learn more about the planets and other objects in our solar system and beyond.

Introduce Target Vocabulary

Tell students they are about to read a selection about our solar system and beyond. Write the target vocabulary words on the board. Model the pronunciation of each word and have student volunteers repeat the word. Discuss the meaning of each word and, if necessary, write the definition next to the word.

Present Graphic Organizer

Provide each student with a copy of Vocabulary Graphic Organizer: Venn Diagram, Teacher Guide page 77. Have students write *Solar System* in the overlap of the circles, *This Is Part of the Solar System* above the left circle, and *The Solar System Is Part of This*, above the right circle. As they read the lesson, have students write the target vocabulary words under the title that seems most appropriate.

Word and Definition Cards
for Lesson 13 are on pages 123 and 124
of the Teacher Guide.

VOCABULARY STRATEGY: Using Illustrations

Illustrations, especially in textbooks, can provide readers with information about unknown words. Have students look at the diagram of the solar system on age 76 and find the orbits of the planets, the asteroid belt, and the comet orbit. Ask students how the illustration at the top of page 77 is helpful. *(It shows the how the sizes of planets compare to each other.)* Remind students to refer to illustrations, here and in other reading, to get a clearer understanding of new words and ideas.

Our Solar System and Beyond

solar system   inner planets   outer planets   comet   light-year
gravity   satellite   asteroid   galaxy   universe

On a clear night, you can see thousands of stars. How much of the universe are you seeing? Read this selection to see if you guessed correctly.

Our Solar System and Beyond

Our Solar System

The **solar system** is the sun and all the planets and other objects that orbit, or move around, the sun. Gravity holds our solar system together. **Gravity** is the force of attraction between any two objects.

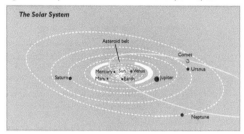

The Solar System

The Inner Planets

The four planets closest to the sun are Mercury, Venus, Earth, and Mars. They are called the **inner planets**. The inner planets have rocky crusts. They are relatively small in size and weight, and they rotate, or spin, slowly.

A **satellite** is an object that moves around a larger object in space. A moon is a satellite that moves around a planet. Mars has two tiny moons that orbit it. Earth has one moon.

 76

Outer Planets

The **outer planets** are the four planets farthest from the sun. They are Jupiter, Saturn, Uranus, and Neptune. The outer planets are giants made mostly of frozen gas. They have many satellites and rings. The outer planets rotate very rapidly but take a long time to orbit the sun.

Relative Sizes of Outer Planets

Asteroids and Comets

Asteroids and comets are also part of our solar system. An **asteroid** is a small solid object of rock and metal. Asteroids are smaller than planets. Many asteroids orbit the sun between Mars and Jupiter. Comets come from the outer edges of the solar system. A **comet** is a ball of rock, dust, and ice that orbits the sun in a huge, oval-shaped path. When a comet travels close to the sun, energy from the sun causes a large bright tail of gases to form.

Milky Way Galaxy and Beyond

A **galaxy** is a large group of stars, planets, moons, asteroids, comets, dust, and gas all held together by gravity. Our sun is one of hundreds of billions of stars in the Milky Way galaxy.

Scientists use a measure called a light-year for distances in space. A **light-year** is the distance light can travel in a year. In our galaxy, the nearest star to the sun is four light-years away. The next nearest galaxy like our own is two million light-years away. There are billions of galaxies in the universe. The **universe** is all the energy and matter that exists in the vastness of space.

The Milky Way galaxy is shaped like a spiral.

My Science Vocabulary

Go to page 98 to list other words you have learned about our solar system and beyond.

Our Solar System and Beyond   77

DURING READING

Read the selection aloud to students, stopping at the end of each paragraph or section. Review any words or concepts that students are having trouble with. Remind students that there is a glossary at the back of their book that contains all of the words that appear in boldfaced type in the lesson.

- Drop a book. Explain that Earth's gravity pulls the book toward it as the book's gravity pulls Earth. See if students can explain that the effect they see is because Earth is much larger. Ask students if any object is not affected by gravity *(no)*.

- Point out that satellites can be natural *(moon)* or objects launched into space to orbit a planet. Ask students which kind of satellite is discussed here *(natural satellite)*.

- Point out the compound *light-year*. Have students explain how each part contributes to the meaning of the term. *(Light is what is measured and a year is the time.)*

- Give students the following terms: *solar system, universe, planet, galaxy.* Have them write a list of the terms in order from largest to smallest *(universe, galaxy, solar system, planet)*.

Have students read the selection again on their own.

AFTER READING

Review Graphic Organizers

Answer any questions students have about the reading selection. Then have students complete or review their graphic organizer and share it with the class.

Summarize

Have students work together to come up with either a written or an oral summary of the lesson. Encourage students to use the target vocabulary words as the basis of their summary. Have students share their summary with the class.

My Science Vocabulary

Encourage students to turn to My Science Vocabulary on page 98 of the student book and use the space provided to add other words about our solar system and beyond.

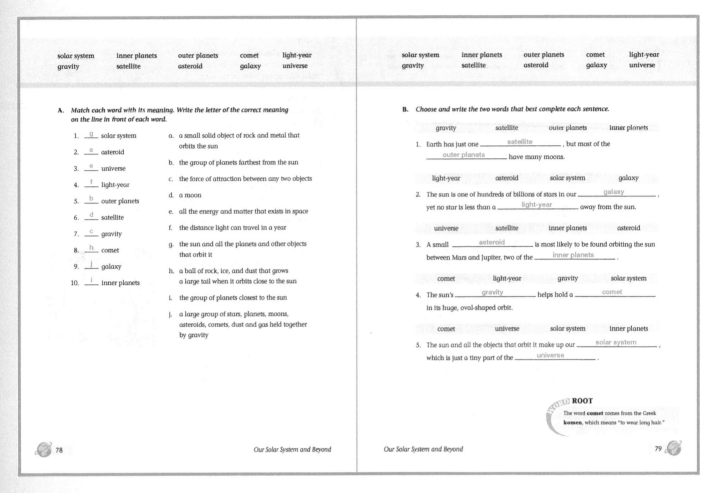

solar system   inner planets   outer planets   comet   light-year
gravity   satellite   asteroid   galaxy   universe

A. Match each word with its meaning. Write the letter of the correct meaning on the line in front of each word.

1. _g_ solar system
2. _a_ asteroid
3. _e_ universe
4. _f_ light-year
5. _b_ outer planets
6. _d_ satellite
7. _c_ gravity
8. _h_ comet
9. _j_ galaxy
10. _i_ inner planets

a. a small solid object of rock and metal that orbits the sun
b. the group of planets farthest from the sun
c. the force of attraction between any two objects
d. a moon
e. all the energy and matter that exists in space
f. the distance light can travel in a year
g. the sun and all the planets and other objects that orbit it
h. a ball of rock, ice, and dust that grows a large tail when it orbits close to the sun
i. the group of planets closest to the sun
j. a large group of stars, planets, moons, asteroids, comets, dust and gas held together by gravity

Our Solar System and Beyond

78

---

solar system   inner planets   outer planets   comet   light-year
gravity   satellite   asteroid   galaxy   universe

B. Choose and write the two words that best complete each sentence.

   gravity   satellite   outer planets   inner planets

1. Earth has just one ___satellite___, but most of the ___outer planets___ have many moons.

   light-year   asteroid   solar system   galaxy

2. The sun is one of hundreds of billions of stars in our ___galaxy___, yet no star is less than a ___light-year___ away from the sun.

   universe   satellite   inner planets   asteroid

3. A small ___asteroid___ is most likely to be found orbiting the sun between Mars and Jupiter, two of the ___inner planets___.

   comet   light-year   gravity   solar system

4. The sun's ___gravity___ helps hold a ___comet___ in its huge, oval-shaped orbit.

   comet   universe   solar system   inner planets

5. The sun and all the objects that orbit it make up our ___solar system___, which is just a tiny part of the ___universe___.

ROOT
The word **comet** comes from the Greek **komen**, which means "to wear long hair."

Our Solar System and Beyond

79

ACTIVITIES A–D

Encourage students to complete as many of the activities as possible. Remind students that they may refer to the Glossary at the back of their book as they complete the activities. Students may work independently, in small groups, or as a class. When students are done, discuss the answers for each activity.

Extensions

These extension ideas allow you to reuse or expand upon the activities. Share them with students who complete the activities before other students, or have students do them for additional practice with the target vocabulary words.

A Put the target vocabulary words in alphabetical order.

B Find the target vocabulary words that have meanings beyond their use in astronomy *(satellite, galaxy, gravity, asteroid, universe)*. Look up and write the dictionary definitions of these words.

WORD ROOT

Ask students to explain how the origin of the word *comet* relates to its description. *(A comet grows a long, hairlike tail when it orbits near the sun.)* Tell students that word roots may relate to words by a characteristic, such as this example, rather than like meanings.

C Write the context clues you used to pick the correct word for each pair of sentences.

D Draw a picture for which one of the sentences could be a good caption.

C. *Write the vocabulary word that best completes each pair of sentences.*

1. Mercury, Venus, Earth, and Mars are the ___inner planets___
   The four planets closest to the sun are the ___inner planets___

2. Earth has one moon, or ___satellite___ .
   Any object that orbits a planet is a ___satellite___ .

3. The sun and the objects that orbit it make up the ___solar system___ .
   The planets and their moons are part of the ___solar system___ .

4. Rock and metal are found in each small ___asteroid___ that orbits the sun.
   An ___asteroid___ may orbit between Jupiter and Mars.

5. All the matter and energy in space makes up the ___universe___ .
   The ___universe___ includes all the galaxies.

6. Jupiter, Saturn, Uranus, and Neptune are the ___outer planets___ .
   The four planets farthest from the sun are the ___outer planets___ .

7. A measure used for distances in space is the ___light-year___ .
   The distance light can travel in a year is a ___light-year___ .

8. The orbit of a ___comet___ is a huge, oval-shaped path.
   The sun's energy causes a ___comet___ to form a bright tail.

9. Stars, planets, moons, asteroids, comets, dust, and gas make up a ___galaxy___
   Our sun is one of hundreds of billions of stars in the Milky Way ___galaxy___ .

10. The force of attraction between objects is ___gravity___ .
    Our solar system and our galaxy are each held together by ___gravity___

Students' answers will vary.

D. *Use each pair of words in a sentence.*

1. inner planets, outer planets
   The inner planets have shorter orbits because they are closer to the sun than the outer planets.

2. asteroid, comet
   An asteroid is a body of rock and metal, but a comet is a ball of rock, dust, and ice that grows a bright tail near the sun.

3. satellite, solar system
   Earth has one satellite, but most of the outer planets of the solar system have many satellites and rings.

4. galaxy, gravity
   The stars, planets, and other objects of a galaxy are held together by gravity.

5. light-year, universe
   The universe is so vast that even a light-year is not a large enough unit to measure the distances.

 Write! ___

Write your response to the prompt on a separate sheet of paper. Use as many vocabulary words as you can in your writing.

If you could take a flight through the universe, what would you find as you traveled?

Write! 🖐️👄👂

Distribute Writing Graphic Organizer: Narrative Map, Teacher Guide page 82. Have students work with a partner or in a small group to brainstorm ideas for writing. They should list themselves as the main character for this first-person narrative. Setting(s) will include all the places they will fly. Main events will include what will occur.

Sample Answer

I start at the blazing sun and watch a comet's long tail form as it orbits the sun. I observe each of the inner planets. I see Earth's one satellite, our moon, held in orbit by gravity. Next, I pass through the asteroid belt. The outer planets look huge until I reach Pluto. Now I leave our solar system, traveling light-year after light-year to other stars in our galaxy. Then I even leave our galaxy to see more of the universe.

TAKE-HOME ACTIVITY 🖐️✏️👄

Assign the Take-Home Activity to students for additional practice with the target vocabulary words. The reproducible Take-Home Activity for Lesson 13 is on page 96 of the Teacher Guide.

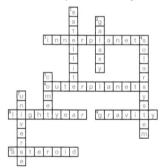

TAKE HOME 13

| solar system | inner planets | outer planets | comet | light-year |
| gravity | satellite | asteroid | galaxy | universe |

Use vocabulary words to complete the puzzle.

Our Solar System and Beyond

ACROSS

3. the four planets closest to the sun
6. the planets farthest from the sun
8. the distance light can travel in a year
9. the force of attraction between any two objects
10. a small solid object of rock and metal

DOWN

1. an object that moves around a larger object in space
2. a large group of stars, planets, moons, asteroids, comets, dust, and gas, held together by gravity
4. the sun and all the objects that orbit around it
5. a ball of rock, dust, and ice
7. all the energy and matter that exists

 Tell someone in your family what you have learned about our solar system and beyond.

Our Solar System and Beyond

LESSON 14

Stars

(Student Book pages 82–87)

Lesson Summary A star forms in a nebula. The life cycle of a star depends on its mass. A low-mass star burns a long time, but then turns into a red giant and finally a white dwarf. As a white dwarf, gases on the surface sometimes explode to create a nova. A high-mass star may become a blue giant and then a supergiant that collapses in a supernova. After a supernova, a high-mass star may become a neutron star, seen as a pulsar, or a black hole.

TARGET VOCABULARY

nebula a huge cloud of gas and dust in space

red giant a large, red, fairly bright star

white dwarf a very small, dense white star

nova a white dwarf that burns much brighter for a time

blue giant a very large, hot, bright star

supergiant a very large, very bright star

supernova a huge explosion caused by the collapse of a supergiant

neutron star a tiny, spinning, dense star

pulsar a neutron star that gives off energy pulses

black hole a region of extreme gravity

COGNATES

Spanish-speaking students may find a discussion of the similarities and differences between English and Spanish cognates helpful.

English	Spanish
nebula	nebulosa
nova	nova
neutron star	estrella de neutrones
pulsar	pulsar

BEFORE READING

Activate Prior Knowledge

Direct students to the title of the lesson. Ask students what they know about stars. Write this sentence starter on the board, "I think stars _____." Then have students take turns completing the sentence, either orally or in writing. Tell students that in this lesson they will discover if their sentences are correct.

Introduce Target Vocabulary

Tell students they are about to read a selection about stars. Write the target vocabulary words on the board. Model the pronunciation of each word and have student volunteers repeat the word. Discuss the meaning of each word and, if necessary, write the definition next to the word.

Present Graphic Organizer

Provide each student with a copy of Vocabulary Graphic Organizer: Venn Diagram, Teacher Guide page 77. Have students title one circle *Small Stars* and one *Large Stars*. As they read the lesson, have students write the target vocabulary words under the title that seems most appropriate. Point out that the overlap of the circles is for words that fit under both titles.

> Word and Definition Cards
> for Lesson 14 are on pages 125 and 126
> of the Teacher Guide.

VOCABULARY STRATEGY: Prefix

Super- is a prefix that can mean "placement above, over, or outside" or "greater in quality, size, or degree." For example, a *superstructure* is built on top of a structure; *supercool* is "to cool a liquid below its freezing point without its freezing." Have students write target vocabulary words with this prefix, as well as the base words (*supergiant, giant* and *supernova, nova*). Have students explain how the prefix *super-* changes the meaning of the base word.

(A nova is a small star that suddenly explodes and increases in brightness; a supernova is the massive explosion of a huge star. A supergiant is a very large star.) Ask students to think of other words with the prefix *super-* (*supermarket, superintendent, superheat, superabundant, superfine, etc.*) Encourage students to add this information to the prefix chart on page 100 of their book.

Stars

LESSON 14

| nebula | white dwarf | blue giant | supernova | pulsar |
| red giant | nova | supergiant | neutron star | black hole |

The star closest to Earth is the sun. All the other stars you can see look like tiny points of light. Would all those stars look like the sun if you could move closer to them? Read this selection to check your answer.

Stars

Our sun is an average-sized, medium-hot star in the middle of its life cycle. Our sun seems as if it would last forever. But all stars change and die.

A star begins life in a **nebula**, a huge cloud of gas and dust in space. The force of gravity pulls together the matter in the nebula to form a young star.

Life Cycle of Average-sized Stars

The life cycle of a star depends on its size. An average-sized star burns a long time. Then the star's center contracts, or shrinks. At the same time, the star's gases expand into a **red giant**, a large red star that is cool but still fairly bright. In time, a red giant collapses. Its center forms a **white dwarf**, a very small, dense white star.

A white dwarf sometimes attracts gases from a nearby star. The gases explode on the star's surface as a nova. A **nova** is a white dwarf that becomes, for a time, much brighter than it was. At the end of its life cycle, a white dwarf cools and stops shining.

Life Cycle of an Average-sized Star

Nebula — Average-sized star — Red giant — White dwarf

82 Stars

Life Cycle of Large Stars

Large stars begin like average-sized stars but burn up faster. A large star may grow into a **blue giant**, a huge, very hot, bright star. When the center of a blue giant contracts, the gases expand into an even brighter **supergiant**. Eventually, the supergiant collapses, causing a huge explosion, or **supernova**. A supernova is the most violent explosion known.

After a supernova, a neutron star or a black hole may form. A **neutron star** is a tiny, rapidly spinning star made from the very dense core left behind by the supergiant. From Earth, a neutron star can be observed as a pulsar. A **pulsar** is a neutron star that gives off evenly spaced pulses of energy. A pulsar's energy seems to blink on and off. A **black hole** is a region with extremely dense matter. Its gravity is so strong that nothing, not even light, can escape from it.

Life Cycle of a Large Star

Nebula — Large star — Blue giant — Supergiant — Supernova — Neutron star — Black hole

My Science Vocabulary

Go to page 98 to list other words you have learned about stars.

Stars 83

DURING READING

Read the selection aloud to students, stopping at the end of each paragraph or section. Review any words or concepts that students are having trouble with. Remind students that there is a glossary at the back of their book that contains all of the words that appear in boldfaced type in the lesson.

- Have students describe what a dwarf and a giant are in children's stories. Point out that a dwarf star, such as a white dwarf, is relatively small like a dwarf; and a large star, such as a red giant or a blue giant, is very large like a giant.

- Refer students to the life-cycle diagrams on pages 82 and 83. Have them describe the steps shown in their own words.

- Point out that *pulsar* comes from *pulse*, "a rhythmic beating." In this case, it is the energy that is rhythmic.

- Have students write a one- or two-sentence description of a black hole. Help them understand that a black hole is black because no light can escape.

Have students read the selection again on their own.

AFTER READING

Review Graphic Organizers

Answer any questions students have about the reading selection. Then have students complete or review their graphic organizer and share it with the class.

Summarize

Have students work together to come up with either a written or an oral summary of the lesson. Encourage students to use the target vocabulary words as the basis of their summary. Have students share their summary with the class.

My Science Vocabulary

Encourage students to turn to My Science Vocabulary on page 98 of the student book and use the space provided to add other words about stars.

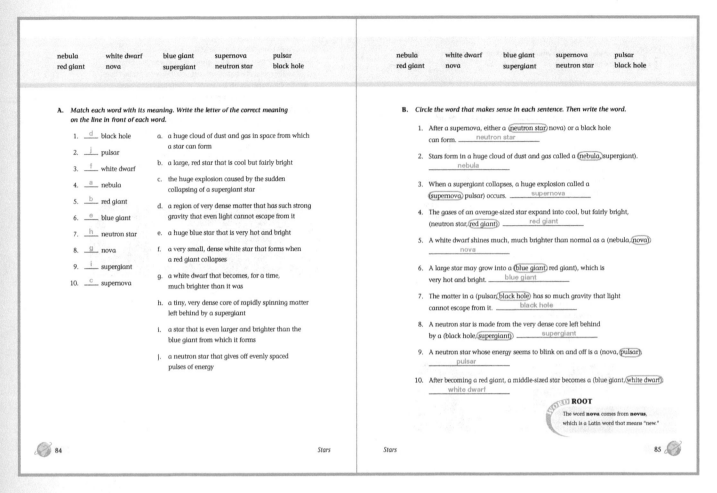

nebula white dwarf blue giant supernova pulsar
red giant nova supergiant neutron star black hole

A. *Match each word with its meaning. Write the letter of the correct meaning on the line in front of each word.*

1. __d__ black hole
2. __j__ pulsar
3. __f__ white dwarf
4. __a__ nebula
5. __b__ red giant
6. __e__ blue giant
7. __h__ neutron star
8. __g__ nova
9. __i__ supergiant
10. __c__ supernova

a. a huge cloud of dust and gas in space from which a star can form

b. a large, red star that is cool but fairly bright

c. the huge explosion caused by the sudden collapsing of a supergiant star

d. a region of very dense matter that has such strong gravity that even light cannot escape from it

e. a huge blue star that is very hot and bright

f. a very small, dense white star that forms when a red giant collapses

g. a white dwarf that becomes, for a time, much brighter than it was

h. a tiny, very dense core of rapidly spinning matter left behind by a supergiant

i. a star that is even larger and brighter than the blue giant from which it forms

j. a neutron star that gives off evenly spaced pulses of energy

84   *Stars*

nebula white dwarf blue giant supernova pulsar
red giant nova supergiant neutron star black hole

B. *Circle the word that makes sense in each sentence. Then write the word.*

1. After a supernova, either a (neutron star / nova) or a black hole can form. ___neutron star___

2. Stars form in a huge cloud of dust and gas called a (nebula / supergiant). ___nebula___

3. When a supergiant collapses, a huge explosion called a (supernova / pulsar) occurs. ___supernova___

4. The gases of an average-sized star expand into cool, but fairly bright, (neutron star / red giant) ___red giant___

5. A white dwarf shines much, much brighter than normal as a (nebula / nova) ___nova___

6. A large star may grow into a (blue giant / red giant), which is very hot and bright. ___blue giant___

7. The matter in a (pulsar / black hole) has so much gravity that light cannot escape from it. ___black hole___

8. A neutron star is made from the very dense core left behind by a (black hole / supergiant) ___supergiant___

9. A neutron star whose energy seems to blink on and off is a (nova / pulsar). ___pulsar___

10. After becoming a red giant, a middle-sized star becomes a (blue giant / white dwarf) ___white dwarf___

ROOT
The word **nova** comes from **novus**, which is a Latin word that means "new."

Stars   85

ACTIVITIES A–D

Encourage students to complete as many of the activities as possible. Remind students that they may refer to the Glossary at the back of their book as they complete the activities. Students may work independently, in small groups, or as a class. When students are done, discuss the answers for each activity.

Extensions

These extension ideas allow you to reuse or expand upon the activities. Share them with students who complete the activities before other students, or have students do them for additional practice with the target vocabulary words.

A Group the target vocabulary words under *Names of Star Types and Stages, Explosions of Stars,* or *Patterns of Stars.*

B Circle all the nouns in the sentences.

WORD ROOT

Explain that people used to think a nova was a new star forming. A supernova may have seemed to be the formation of a huge, or super, new star.

C Renumber the sentences to reflect the order in which the target vocabulary words would appear in a dictionary.

D Use the sentences to write a question for each of the target vocabulary words in each pair. The answer to your question should be the vocabulary word.

nebula   white dwarf   blue giant   supernova   pulsar
red giant   nova   supergiant   neutron star   black hole

C. *Choose the correct vocabulary word to complete each sentence.*

1. The most violent explosion known is a _____supernova_____, which occurs when a supergiant collapses.

2. When the center of a blue giant contracts, its gases expand into a _____supergiant_____.

3. A white dwarf may become a much brighter _____nova_____ before it cools and stops shining.

4. One possible result of a supernova is a very tiny, rapidly spinning _____neutron star_____

5. A new star is born in a _____nebula_____.

6. An average-sized star burns a very long time before its gases expand into a _____red giant_____.

7. A neutron star can be observed from Earth as a _____pulsar_____.

8. A huge, very hot blue star is a _____blue giant_____.

9. A supernova creates either a neutron star or a _____black hole_____.

10. In time, a red giant cools and collapses into a _____white dwarf_____.

 86

Stars

---

nebula   white dwarf   blue giant   supernova   pulsar
red giant   nova   supergiant   neutron star   black hole

Students' answers will vary.

D. *Use each pair of words in a sentence.*

1. neutron star, pulsar
   A neutron star can be observed as a pulsar from Earth.

2. black hole, supernova
   After a supernova, a black hole may form.

3. nova, white dwarf
   Explosions on the surface of a white dwarf cause the star to be a nova.

4. red giant, blue giant
   A red giant is a cool, bright star, but a blue giant is a hot, bright star.

5. nebula, supergiant
   A large star begins its life cycle as a nebula and eventually grows into a supergiant.

 Write! _____
Write your response to the prompt on a separate sheet of paper. Use as many vocabulary words as you can in your writing.
Tell the life story of an average-sized star like the sun or the life story of a star larger than the sun.

Stars

87

Write!

Distribute Writing Graphic Organizer: Main Idea and Details Chart, Teacher Guide page 80. Tell students to write a main idea about the life story of an average-sized star in the Main Idea box labeled 1. Have them write a main idea about the life story of a large star in the Main Idea box labeled 2. Have them list details in the first Details box for main idea 1 and in the second Details box for main idea 2.

Sample Answer

    I begin my journey in a nebula. First, I follow a smaller star I know. In time, this star becomes a huge red giant. Then it collapses into a white dwarf. Maybe it burns brightly as a nova for awhile.

    I go back to the nebula to follow a blue giant. In time, it explodes in a huge supernova. I hope it becomes a black hole, but this time what's left is a neutron star. From Earth, it is a pulsar, blinking on and off.

TAKE-HOME ACTIVITY

Assign the Take-Home Activity to students for additional practice with the target vocabulary words. The reproducible Take-Home Activity for Lesson 14 is on page 97 of the Teacher Guide.

TAKE HOME 14

nebula   white dwarf   blue giant   supernova   pulsar
red giant   nova   supergiant   neutron star   black hole

Use vocabulary words to complete the puzzle.

Stars

(crossword puzzle with answers: black hole, supergiant, nebula, neutron star, supernova, red giant, blue giant, white dwarf, pulsar, nova)

ACROSS

2. a region of extremely dense matter
4. a very bright, very large star
5. a huge cloud of gas and dust in space
7. a tiny, dense core of matter left after a supernova
8. a huge explosion
9. a large red star that is cool but fairly bright

DOWN

1. a huge, very hot blue star
3. what forms when a red giant collapses
6. a neutron star giving off pulses of energy
7. a white dwarf shining much brighter

 Tell someone in your family what you have learned about stars.

©Curriculum Associates, LLC *Passwords: Science Vocabulary, Earth Science, Lesson 14*   97

LESSON 15

Earth and the Moon in Motion

(Student Book pages 88–93)

Lesson Summary Earth makes one revolution around the sun each year, and one rotation on its axis each day. (Earth's axis has a 23.5 degree tilt.) The moon's revolution around Earth causes tides, the moon's phases, and eclipses. The moon's phases are waxing from new moon to full moon, and waning from full moon to new moon. A lunar eclipse occurs when the Earth blocks the sun's light from reaching the moon. A solar eclipse occurs when the moon passes between Earth and the sun.

TARGET VOCABULARY

revolution the movement of one object in space around another object

rotation the spinning of an object on its axis

axis an imaginary line around which an object rotates

tilt slant

tides the rise and fall of the level of the ocean

phase a pattern of the moon's light as seen from Earth

waxing growing larger

waning getting smaller

lunar eclipse the blocking of the sun's light on the moon by Earth

solar eclipse the blocking of the sun's light on Earth by the moon

COGNATES

Spanish-speaking students may find a discussion of the similarities and differences between English and Spanish cognates helpful.

English	Spanish
revolution	revolución
rotation	rotación
phase	fase
lunar eclipse	eclipse lunar
solar eclipse	eclipse solar

BEFORE READING

Activate Prior Knowledge

Ask students how the moon changes. What do they think causes the changes they observe? Have them write their ideas. Tell them one thing they will read about in this lesson is the movements of Earth and its moon that cause the moon's changing shape.

Introduce Target Vocabulary

Tell students they are about to read a selection about Earth and the moon in motion. Write the target vocabulary words on the board. Model the pronunciation of each word and have student volunteers repeat the word. Discuss the meaning of each word and, if necessary, write the definition next to the word.

Present Graphic Organizer

Provide each student with a copy of Vocabulary Graphic Organizer: Venn Diagram, Teacher Guide page 77. Have students title one circle *Earth* and one *Moon*. As they read the lesson, have students write the target vocabulary words related only to Earth in the circle titled *Earth*, and those related only to the moon in the part titled *Moon*. In the overlap of the circles, students write words that apply to both titles.

Word and Definition Cards
for Lesson 15 are on pages 127 and 128
of the Teacher Guide.

VOCABULARY STRATEGY: Suffixes and Roots

Tell students that the suffix -ar is used to make adjectives that mean "like or relating to." Ask students to think of a few more adjectives ending in the suffix -ar; for example, *polar (of the pole)*, *rectangular (like a rectangle)*, and *circular (like a circle)*. Ask students to pick the two target vocabulary words that end in the suffix -ar (*solar*, *lunar*). Students who know Spanish may recognize the roots of these words. The Spanish word for *sun* is "*sol*" and the Spanish word for *moon* is "*luna*." Have students use this information to figure out the meanings of *lunar (of or relating to the moon)* and *solar (of or relating to the sun)*.

Earth and the Moon in Motion

revolution   axis   tides   waxing   lunar eclipse
rotation   tilt   phase   waning   solar eclipse

You have seen the moon changing its shape each month as it moves across the sky. What causes the moon's shape to change? What other changes does the moon's movement cause? Read this selection to find out.

Earth and the Moon in Motion

Earth's Movements

Earth is always moving in space. Each year, Earth makes one complete revolution around the sun. A **revolution** is the movement of one body in space around another body.

Every 24 hours, Earth also makes one complete rotation. A **rotation** is the spinning of an object on an axis. An **axis** is an imaginary line. Earth's axis goes from the North Pole to the South Pole and has a **tilt**, or slant.

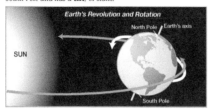

Earth's Revolution and Rotation
North Pole — Earth's axis
SUN
South Pole

The Moon's Movements

Earth's moon moves in ways similar to Earth. The moon rotates on an axis. The moon revolves around Earth. As the moon circles Earth, gravity between them causes tides. **Tides** are the daily rise and fall of the level of the ocean. Tides can be seen near the shore.

88   Earth and the Moon in Motion

Phases of the Moon

The sun always lights half the moon. But from Earth, the amount of the moon that is lighted seems to change. Each changing pattern of light on the moon as seen from Earth is a **phase**.

When the moon is in the new moon phase, the moon is between Earth and the sun. No sunlight shows on the side of the moon facing Earth. So the moon cannot be seen. As the moon keeps revolving, the lighted part of the moon that is seen from Earth begins **waxing**, or growing larger. The moon continues waxing until the full moon phase.

In the full moon phase, the moon is on the opposite side of Earth from the sun. People can see the fully lit side of the moon, which appears as a complete circle. Then the light on the moon begins **waning**, or getting smaller, until the next new moon. This cycle from new moon to new moon takes 29.5 days.

Phases of the Moon
Sunlight
New moon
Waxing crescent — Waning crescent
First quarter — Last quarter
Waxing gibbous — Waning gibbous
Full moon

Eclipses

An eclipse is a blocking of light. A **lunar eclipse** occurs when Earth blocks the sun's light from reaching the moon. Earth moves between the full moon and the sun, darkening the moon for a short time.

A **solar eclipse** occurs when the moon blocks the light of the sun from reaching places on Earth. The new moon moves between Earth and the sun, and places on Earth over which the shadow passes have a solar eclipse.

Lunar Eclipse
Earth's shadow
Sun — Earth — Moon

Solar Eclipse
Moon's shadow
Sun — Moon — Earth

 My Science Vocabulary
Go to page 98 to list other words you have learned about Earth and the moon in motion.

Earth and the Moon in Motion   89

DURING READING

Read the selection aloud to students, stopping at the end of each paragraph or section. Review any words or concepts that students are having trouble with. Remind students that there is a glossary at the back of their book that contains all of the words that appear in boldfaced type in the lesson.

- For each target vocabulary word listed below, have one student with a large flashlight be the sun, one student be the Earth, and one be the moon. Help the students move correctly to model revolution, rotation, phases, lunar eclipse, and solar eclipse.

- Point out that *waxing* and *waning* are from the verbs *wax*, "to grow larger," and *wane*, "to grow smaller." Both are from Old English. Tell students that waxing in this sense is not related to the noun *wax*.

- Direct students' attention to the diagram of the phases of the moon on page 89. Help students visualize that the center circle shows how the moon would look from space. The sun lights the half of the moon facing it. The outer circle shows how the moon looks from Earth at that point in its orbit.

- Explain that the Earth's tilt *(noun)* comes from the way Earth tilts *(verb.)* Have students write two sentences, one using the noun *tilt* and one the verb *tilts*.

Have students read the selection again on their own.

AFTER READING

Review Graphic Organizers
Answer any questions students have about the reading selection. Then have students complete or review their graphic organizer and share it with the class.

Summarize
Have students work together to come up with either a written or an oral summary of the lesson. Encourage students to use the target vocabulary words as the basis of their summary. Have students share their summary with the class.

My Science Vocabulary
Encourage students to turn to My Science Vocabulary on page 98 of the student book and use the space provided to add other words about Earth and the moon in motion.

Earth and the Moon in Motion

| revolution | axis | tides | waxing | lunar eclipse |
| rotation | tilt | phase | waning | solar eclipse |

A. Fill in the blanks with the correct vocabulary word.

1. an imaginary line around which an object spins
   a x i s

2. growing larger, as when the moon goes from the new moon phase to the full moon phase
   w a x i n g

3. the blocking of the sun's light by the moon from places on Earth
   s o l a r   e c l i p s e

4. a slant
   t i l t

5. the movement of one body in space around another body
   r e v o l u t i o n

6. the blocking of the sun's light by Earth from the moon
   l u n a r   e c l i p s e

7. a changing pattern of light on the moon as seen from Earth
   p h a s e

8. the daily rise and fall of the level of the ocean
   t i d e s

9. the spinning of an object on an axis
   r o t a t i o n

10. growing smaller, as when the moon goes from the full moon phase to the new moon phase
    w a n i n g

90   Earth and the Moon in Motion

| revolution | axis | tides | waxing | lunar eclipse |
| rotation | tilt | phase | waning | solar eclipse |

B. Circle the word that makes sense in each sentence. Then write the word.

1. When the moon is (waxing, waning), the lighted part of the moon from Earth is growing. _____waxing_____

2. Like Earth, the moon rotates on an (phase, axis). _____axis_____

3. A year is the time it takes Earth to make one (revolution, rotation) around the sun. _____revolution_____

4. The new moon is a (phase, tilt) in which the moon is between Earth and the Sun. _____phase_____

5. During a (lunar eclipse, solar eclipse), the full moon looks dark for a short time. _____lunar eclipse_____

6. The axis of Earth has a slant, or (revolution, tilt). _____tilt_____

7. Every day, ocean (rotation, tides) can be seen near the shore. _____tides_____

8. After the full moon, the light on the moon begins (waning, waxing). _____waning_____

9. When the moon moves between Earth and the sun, it can cause a (solar eclipse, lunar eclipse). _____solar eclipse_____

10. The spinning of Earth on its axis is a (phase, rotation). _____rotation_____

WORD ROOT
The word **axis** is from the Latin word **axis**, which means "axle."

Earth and the Moon in Motion   91

ACTIVITIES A–D

Encourage students to complete as many of the activities as possible. Remind students that they may refer to the Glossary at the back of their book as they complete the activities. Students may work independently, in small groups, or as a class. When students are done, discuss the answers for each activity.

Extensions

These extension ideas allow you to reuse or expand upon the activities. Share them with students who complete the activities before other students, or have students do them for additional practice with the target vocabulary words.

A Group the target vocabulary words by the total number of syllables, from one syllable to four syllables.

B Determine and explain which target vocabulary words suggest actions and effects that can best be observed from Earth, which are better observed from space, and which could be seen from Earth and space.

C Rewrite each sentence by changing the order of the information.

D Draw and label a diagram to illustrate one of the sentences.

WORD ROOT

Ask students to explain the words *hub* and *axle*. *(The hub is the center of a wheel, fan, or propeller; the axle is the shaft on which a wheel spins.)* Ask how these words are like the axis of Earth. *(Earth spins on its axis.)* Then have a student demonstrate and explain "spinning on an axis."

revolution	axis	tides	waxing	lunar eclipse
rotation	tilt	phase	waning	solar eclipse

C. *Choose the correct vocabulary word to complete each sentence.*

1. The imaginary line that goes from the North Pole to the South Pole is Earth's _____ axis _____ .

2. When the moon is _____ waxing _____ , its phases are going from new moon to full moon.

3. Earth spins on an axis that has a _____ tilt _____ .

4. Gravity between the moon and Earth causes daily _____ tides _____ .

5. Half the moon is always lit by the sun, but from Earth we see a new moon, a full moon, or some other _____ phase _____ .

6. When Earth moves between the full moon and the sun, a _____ lunar eclipse _____ occurs.

7. When Earth orbits the sun, it is making a _____ revolution _____ .

8. When the moon goes from the full moon phase to the new moon phase, the moon is _____ waning _____ .

9. Every 24 hours, Earth makes one complete _____ rotation _____ on its axis.

10. When the new moon blocks the sun's light from reaching places on Earth, a _____ solar eclipse _____ occurs.

92   *Earth and the Moon in Motion*

---

revolution	axis	tides	waxing	lunar eclipse
rotation	tilt	phase	waning	solar eclipse

Students' answers will vary.

D. *Use each pair of words in a sentence.*

1. waxing, waning
   When the moon is waxing, the phases are growing larger, and when the moon is waning, the phases are growing smaller.

2. solar eclipse, lunar eclipse
   A solar eclipse is a blocking of the sun's light by the moon, and a lunar eclipse is the blocking of the sun's light by Earth.

3. axis, tilt
   The axis of Earth has a tilt.

4. rotation, phase
   The moon's rotation does not change the phase of the moon seen on Earth.

5. tides, revolution
   As the moon makes a complete revolution around Earth, the gravity between the moon and Earth causes tides.

Write!

Write your response to the prompt on a separate sheet of paper. Use as many vocabulary words as you can in your writing.

If you could watch the sun, moon, and Earth from space, what kinds of movements could you observe? What are the effects of those movements?

Earth and the Moon in Motion   93

Write!

Distribute Writing Graphic Organizer: Idea Wheel, Teacher Guide page 81. Tell students to write *Sun, Moon,* and *Earth* in the center of the wheel. Then on the spokes of the wheel, they should list/describe the movements and effects of movements they would observe. Tell students they may add spokes to the wheel, if necessary.

Sample Answer

     From space, I could see Earth's revolution around the sun and Earth's rotation on its axis. As I watch the moon revolve around Earth, I could see how people on Earth would see the waxing and the waning of the moon in its phases. I would see tides rise and fall. Sometimes, the new moon would move between Earth and the sun for a solar eclipse. Later, Earth would move between the sun and the full moon for a lunar eclipse.

TAKE-HOME ACTIVITY

Assign the Take-Home Activity to students for additional practice with the target vocabulary words. The reproducible Take-Home Activity for Lesson 15 is on page 98 of the Teacher Guide.

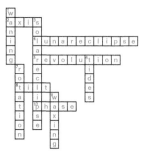

TAKE HOME 15

revolution	axis	tides	waxing	lunar eclipse
rotation	tilt	phase	waning	solar eclipse

Use vocabulary words to complete the puzzle.

Earth and the Moon in Motion

ACROSS

2. an imaginary line on which an object rotates
4. the blocking of the sun's light on the moon by Earth
5. the movement of one object in space around another object
8. the slant of the axis
10. a pattern of the moon's light as seen from Earth

DOWN

1. the growing smaller of the lighted part of the moon that is seen from Earth
3. the blocking of the sun's light on Earth by the moon
6. the rise and fall of the level of the ocean
7. the spinning of an object on its axis
9. the growing larger of the lighted part of the moon that is seen from Earth

Tell someone in your family what you have learned about Earth and the moon in motion.

Earth and the Moon in Motion   75

Vocabulary Graphic Organizer: Word Web

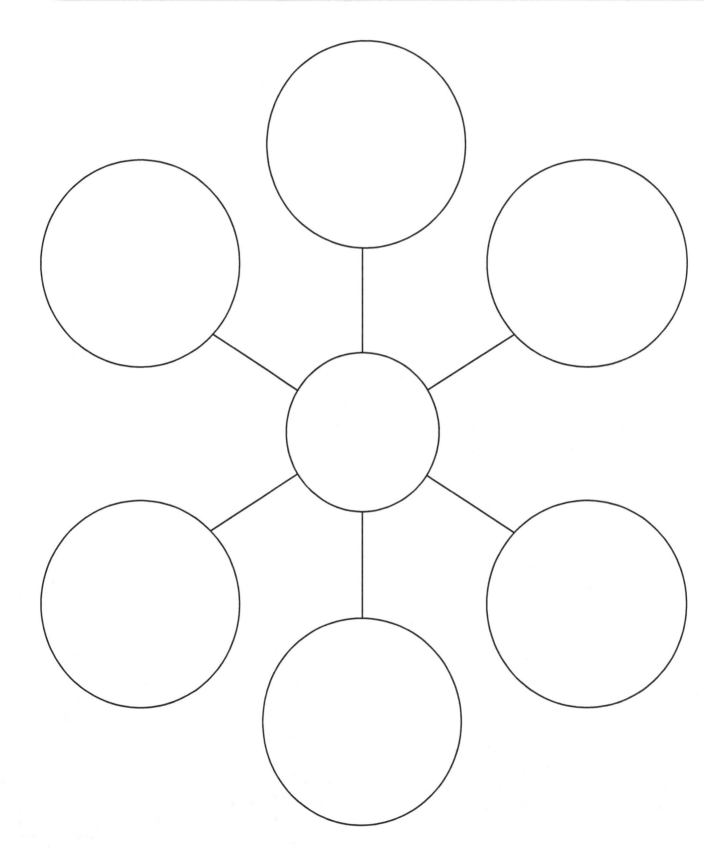

Vocabulary Graphic Organizer: Venn Diagram

_____   _____

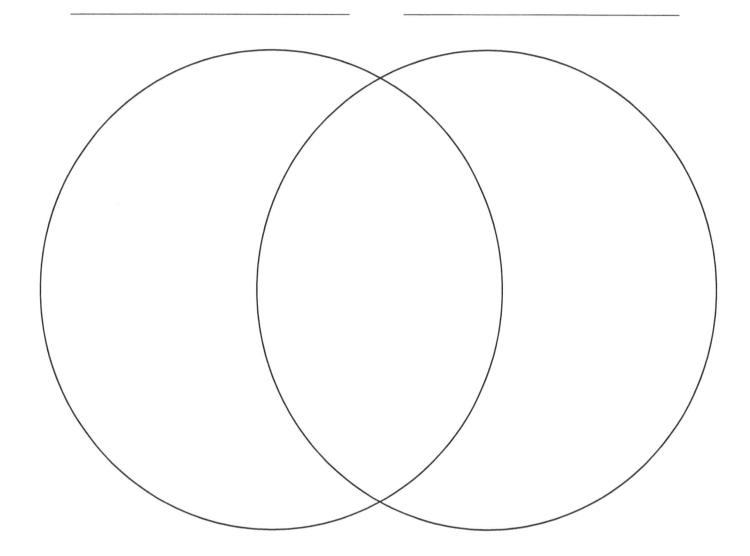

Vocabulary Graphic Organizer: Four Square

_____

Vocabulary Graphic Organizer: Cycle

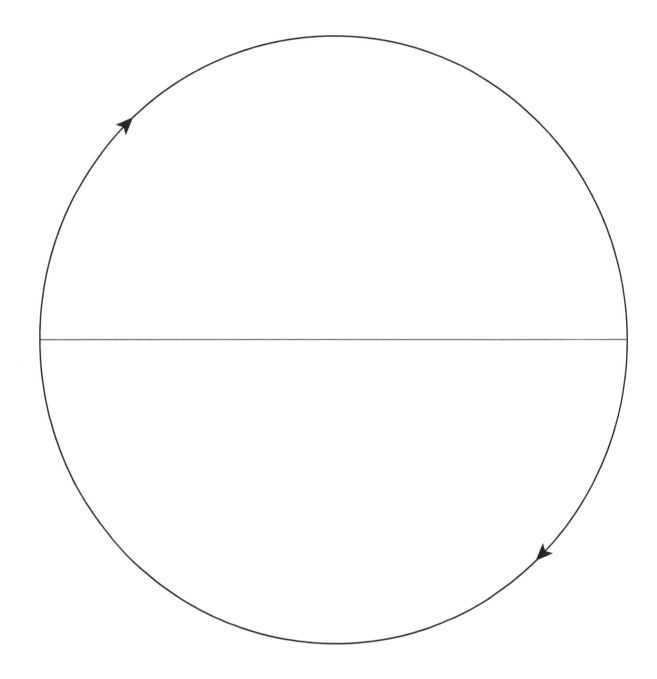

Name _____ Date _____

 # Writing Graphic Organizer: Main Idea and Details Chart

Main Idea	Details
1. _____ _____ _____ _____ _____ _____	_____ _____ _____ _____ _____
2. _____ _____ _____ _____ _____ _____	_____ _____ _____ _____ _____
3. _____ _____ _____ _____ _____ _____	_____ _____ _____ _____ _____

Writing Graphic Organizer: Idea Wheel

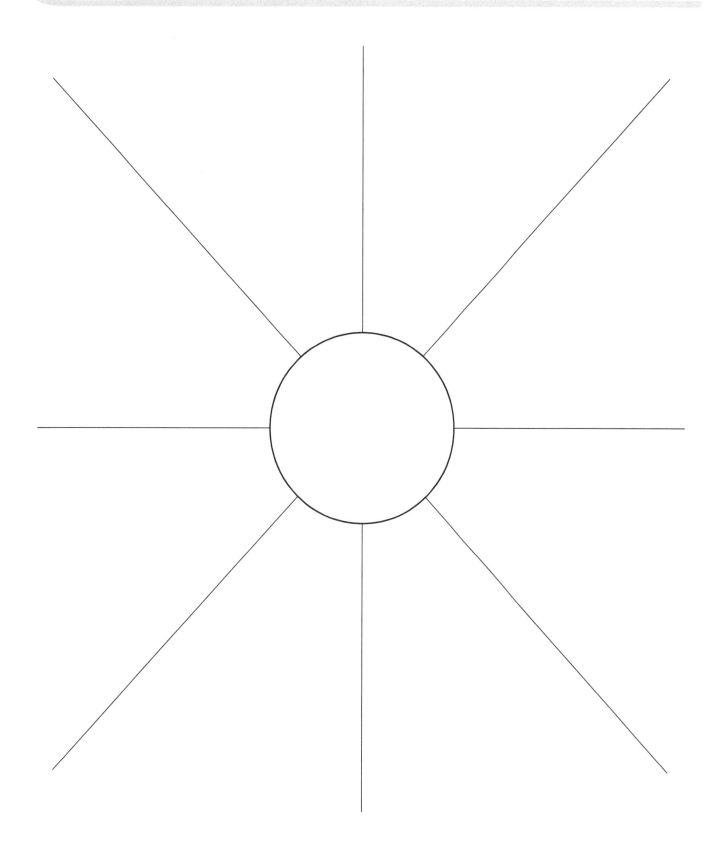

Writing Graphic Organizer: Narrative Map

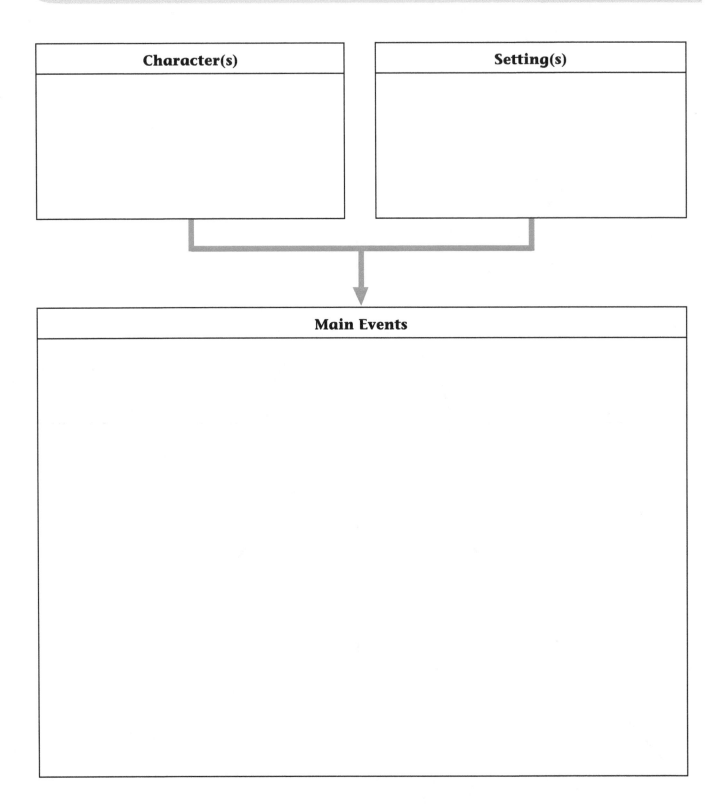

Character(s)	Setting(s)

Main Events

Writing Graphic Organizer: Sequence Chart

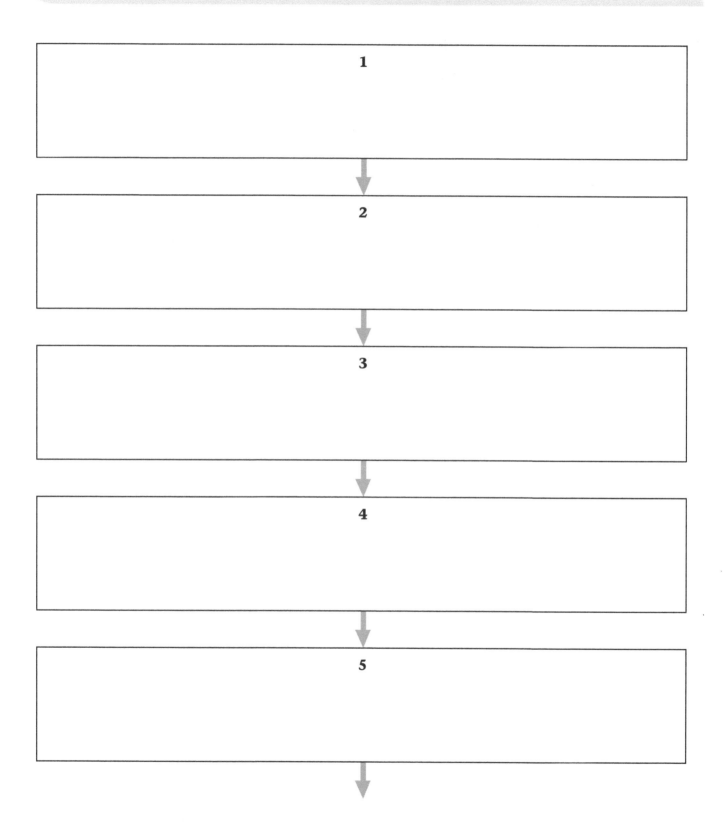

1

2

3

4

5

| continental crust | mantle | molten | topsoil | subsoil |
| oceanic crust | outer core | inner core | humus | bedrock |

Use vocabulary words to complete the puzzle.

Earth's Structure

ACROSS

1 the layer of soil under the topsoil

7 the part of Earth's crust under the continents

9 the part of Earth's crust under the oceans

10 the upper layer of soil

DOWN

2 the solid layer of crust that seems firmly attached to Earth

3 the layer of molten metal just below the mantle

4 the layer of Earth below the crust

5 so hot it becomes liquid

6 the layer of solid metal at the very center of Earth

8 decayed plant and animal matter

 Tell someone in your family what you have learned about Earth's structure.

lithosphere   convection current   ridge   rift

plate   continental drift   folding   seafloor spreading

plate tectonics   fault

Use vocabulary words to complete the puzzle.

Earth's Moving Plates

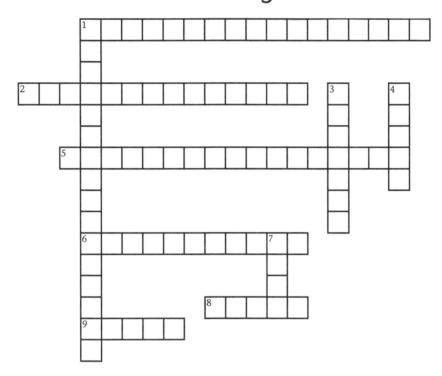

ACROSS

1 the slow up-and-down movement of rock in the soft part of Earth's mantle

2 the model that explains the movement of Earth's plates

5 the process of oceanic plates moving apart at a rift

6 the solid outer part of Earth

8 one section of lithosphere

9 a break in Earth's crust

DOWN

1 the movement of Earth's plates toward and away from each other

3 the bending up of Earth's crust where plates push together

4 a long row of sharp mountains

7 a deep underwater valley where Earth's plates move apart

Tell someone in your family what you have learned about Earth's moving plates.

fault line   focus   epicenter   magnitude   tremor
shock waves   seismic waves   seismograph   Richter scale   aftershock

Use vocabulary words to complete the puzzle.

Earthquakes

ACROSS

1 shock waves from an earthquake

3 the point underground where an earthquake begins

4 the size and strength of an earthquake

5 a mild earthquake

6 a tool to measure and record an earthquake's magnitude

8 the point on Earth's surface right above the focus

DOWN

2 a smaller earthquake that follows a large earthquake

3 the line of the fault on Earth's surface

6 strong waves of energy

7 a scale for measuring an earthquake's magnitude

Tell someone in your family what you have learned about earthquakes.

©Curriculum Associates, LLC *Passwords: Science Vocabulary, Earth Science, Lesson 3*

| magma | lava | | fissure | crater | dormant volcano |
| vent | volcanic eruption | | cone | active volcano | extinct volcano |

Use vocabulary words to complete the puzzle.

Volcanoes

ACROSS

1 a volcano that is erupting or has erupted within the past 10,000 years

5 a long crack in Earth's crust out of which magma flows

6 molten rock below Earth's surface

8 a volcano that is not active or extinct

10 magma that reaches Earth's surface

DOWN

2 a mountain that forms from repeated volcanic eruptions

3 the flowing or bursting out of magma, gases, or ash from a volcano

4 a volcano that has not erupted for 10,000 years

7 an opening of a volcano at the surface

9 a bowl-shaped hole at the top of a volcanic cone

Tell someone in your family what you have learned about volcanoes.

igneous rock   metamorphic rock   erosion   deposition
sedimentary rock   physical weathering   transportation   rock cycle
sediment   chemical weathering

Use vocabulary words to complete the puzzle.

Changes and Forces in the Rock Cycle

ACROSS

1 all the changes rock goes through

3 rock formed from layers of sediment

6 rock formed from heat and pressure

7 the carrying of rock to a new place

8 the breaking down of rock into small pieces

9 bits of rock broken off from larger rock

10 rock formed from hardened magma

DOWN

2 the breaking down of rock by chemicals

4 the wearing away of rocks and sediment by gravity, wind, water, and ice

5 the dropping of rocks and sediment in a new place

Tell someone in your family what you have learned about changes and forces in the rock cycle.

| fossil | decay | dissolve | mold | trace fossil |
| fossilization | preserved | impression | cast | fossil record |

Use vocabulary words to complete the puzzle.

Fossils

ACROSS

2 marks made by the movement of an ancient animal

3 the process of forming fossils

7 to break down and wash away

8 a fossil formed when minerals fill a mold

9 to rot

DOWN

1 kept whole

3 the remains or traces of an ancient plant or animal

4 an image pressed into matter

5 all the fossils taken together

6 the hollow shape of a plant or animal left in rock

Tell someone in your family what you have learned about fossils.

Use vocabulary words to complete the puzzle.

Features of Minerals

ACROSS

2 having a dull luster

4 the color of the powder left by a mineral scratched on a special plate

5 the shine of a mineral

7 made of more than one element

8 a regular repeating shape with smooth sides

10 a mineral made up of only one type of matter

DOWN

1 an inorganic solid occurring naturally in the earth

3 having a shiny luster like a metal

6 having no living matter

9 the quality of a mineral to split along a smooth inner surface

Tell someone in your family what you have learned about the features of minerals.

natural resource   nonrenewable resource   recycling   pollutant

inexhaustible resource   fossil fuel   preservation   acid rain

renewable resource   conservation

Use vocabulary words to complete the puzzle.

Protecting Earth's Resources

ACROSS

7 a resource, like the sun, that cannot be used up

8 a chemical from human activities that harms natural resources

9 protection of natural resources by using less of them

10 using materials from used goods to make new goods

DOWN

1 a resource that cannot be replaced

2 a resource that can be replaced

3 oil, coal, or natural gas

4 a pollutant made of acid from factory smoke in rain

5 something found in nature that people use

6 protection of natural resources by not using them

Tell someone in your family what you have learned about protecting Earth's resources.

atmosphere   water vapor   oxygen   ozone layer   thermosphere

troposphere   nitrogen   stratosphere   mesosphere   exosphere

Use vocabulary words to complete the puzzle.

Earth's Atmosphere

ACROSS

2 the top and widest layer of the atmosphere

5 the layer of atmosphere right above the mesosphere

7 water in the form of a gas

9 a gas that makes up 21% of the troposphere

DOWN

1 the layer of atmosphere above the stratosphere

3 all the air surrounding Earth

4 the layer of atmosphere closest to Earth's surface

6 the layer of atmosphere above the troposphere

8 the layer in the stratosphere that contains a type of oxygen that absorbs harmful rays of the sun

10 a gas in air that makes up 78% of the troposphere

Tell someone in your family what you have learned about Earth's atmosphere.

evaporation   condensation   surface water   watershed   aquifer
humidity   precipitation   runoff   groundwater   water table

Use vocabulary words to complete the puzzle.

Earth's Water Systems

ACROSS

2 the change from a gas to a liquid

6 water falling to Earth as a liquid or a solid

7 the height of water under the ground

8 an underground layer of rock filled with groundwater

9 precipitation that has reached Earth's surface

10 water that flows on top of the land

DOWN

1 water that is beneath Earth's surface

3 the change from a liquid to a gas

4 the amount of water vapor in the air

5 the land area drained by a river

Tell someone in your family what you have learned about Earth's water systems.

ocean floor   submarine canyon   seamount   trench
continental shelf   continental rise   oceanic ridge   subduction zone
continental slope   abyssal plain

Use vocabulary words to complete the puzzle.

The Ocean Floor

ACROSS

1 the ocean floor between the continental shelf and continental rise

2 the part of the ocean floor between the continental slope and the abyssal plain

4 a long chain of mountains on the ocean floor

5 the fairly level deep-ocean floor

7 a deep underwater valley on the continental slope

8 a very deep, wide valley that forms on the ocean floor

DOWN

1 the underwater land at the edge of a continent

3 an area where one plate of the ocean floor is sliding under another

4 the land under the oceans

6 an underwater volcanic mountain

Tell someone in your family what you have learned about the ocean floor.

climate   front   stratus clouds   air pressure   trade winds
air mass   cirrus clouds   cumulus clouds   westerlies   jet stream

Use vocabulary words to complete the puzzle.

Earth's Changing Weather

ACROSS

2 puffy, white clouds

3 the force of air pushing down on Earth

4 where the edges of two air masses meet

5 the average weather over a long period of time

8 two wind belts above and below the equator

9 low, gray clouds

DOWN

1 large belts of wind that blow west to east

2 high, thin, icy clouds

6 a huge body of air with the same features throughout

7 a narrow band of very strong winds that blow west to east

Tell someone in your family what you have learned about Earth's changing weather.

solar system   inner planets   outer planets   comet   light-year

gravity   satellite   asteroid   galaxy   universe

Use vocabulary words to complete the puzzle.

Our Solar System and Beyond

ACROSS

3 the four planets closest to the sun

6 the planets farthest from the sun

8 the distance light can travel in a year

9 the force of attraction between any two objects

10 a small solid object of rock and metal

DOWN

1 an object that moves around a larger object in space

2 a large group of stars, planets, moons, asteroids, comets, dust, and gas, held together by gravity

4 the sun and all the objects that orbit around it

5 a ball of rock, dust, and ice

7 all the energy and matter that exists

Tell someone in your family what you have learned about our solar system and beyond.

TAKE HOME 14

| nebula | white dwarf | blue giant | supernova | pulsar |
| red giant | nova | supergiant | neutron star | black hole |

Use vocabulary words to complete the puzzle.

Stars

ACROSS

2 a region of extremely dense matter

4 a very bright, very large star

5 a huge cloud of gas and dust in space

7 a tiny, dense core of matter left after a supernova

8 a huge explosion

9 a large red star that is cool but fairly bright

DOWN

1 a huge, very hot blue star

3 what forms when a red giant collapses

6 a neutron star giving off pulses of energy

7 a white dwarf shining much brighter

Tell someone in your family what you have learned about stars.

| revolution | axis | tides | waxing | lunar eclipse |
| rotation | tilt | phase | waning | solar eclipse |

Use vocabulary words to complete the puzzle.

Earth and the Moon in Motion

ACROSS

2 an imaginary line on which an object rotates

4 the blocking of the sun's light on the moon by Earth

5 the movement of one object in space around another object

8 the slant of the axis

10 a pattern of the moon's light as seen from Earth

DOWN

1 the growing smaller of the lighted part of the moon that is seen from Earth

3 the blocking of the sun's light on Earth by the moon

6 the rise and fall of the level of the ocean

7 the spinning of an object on its axis

9 the growing larger of the lighted part of the moon that is seen from Earth

Tell someone in your family what you have learned about Earth and the moon in motion.

©Curriculum Associates, LLC *Passwords: Science Vocabulary, Earth Science, Lesson 15*

continental crust	inner core
oceanic crust	topsoil
mantle	humus
outer core	subsoil
molten	bedrock

the layer of solid rock at the very center of Earth

the part of Earth's crust that makes up the land, or continents

the upper layer of soil

the part of Earth's crust that is under the oceans

decayed plant and animal matter

the layer of Earth below the crust

the layer of soil below the topsoil

the layer of molten iron and nickel just below Earth's mantle

the solid layer of crust that seems firmly attached to Earth

so hot it becomes liquid

 Passwords: Science Vocabulary, Earth Science, Lesson 1—Word Cards

lithosphere	fault
plate	ridge
plate tectonics	folding
convection current	rift
continental drift	seafloor spreading

a break in Earth's crust

the solid outer part of Earth, consisting of the crust and the top part of the mantle

a long row of sharp mountains that can form at a rift

a section of the lithosphere

the bending upward of Earth's crust to form mountains, caused by two plates pushing together

the model that explains how Earth's plates create landforms as they move

a deep underwater valley that forms when Earth's plates move apart

the up-and-down movement of soft rock within Earth's mantle, which is caused by uneven heating

the process by which molten rock flows up and out through a rift to form ridges of new crust

the slow movement of Earth's plates that carry continents or parts of continents toward or away from one another

 Passwords: Science Vocabulary, Earth Science, Lesson 2—Word Cards

fault line

seismograph

shock waves

magnitude

focus

Richter scale

seismic
waves

tremor

epicenter

aftershock

a tool that measures and records seismic waves

the line where a fault shows on Earth's surface

the strength of an earthquake

strong energy waves

a scale to measure earthquake magnitude

the point underground where an earthquake begins

an earthquake that causes a small shaking

shock waves produced by an earthquake

a smaller earthquake that follows a large earthquake

the point on Earth's surface directly above the focus of an earthquake

magma	cone
vent	crater
lava	active volcano
volcanic eruption	dormant volcano
fissure	extinct volcano

a mountain that forms from repeated volcanic eruptions

molten rock below Earth's surface

a bowl-shaped hole at the top of the cone, or volcanic mountain

an opening through which magma from a volcano reaches the surface

a volcano that is erupting now or has erupted within the past 10,000 years

magma that has reached the surface, where it cools and hardens into volcanic rock

a volcano that has not erupted recently but may still erupt

the flowing of magma, gases, or volcanic rock from a volcano

a volcano that has not erupted for 10,000 years

a long crack in Earth's crust through which magma flows out gently

igneous rock	chemical weathering
sedimentary rock	erosion
sediment	transportation
metamorphic rock	deposition
physical weathering	rock cycle

the breaking down of rock by chemicals that change the chemical makeup of the rock

rock formed from magma that has hardened

the wearing away of rocks and sediment

rock formed from layers of sediment and other matter squeezed and cemented together

the carrying of weathered rocks and sediment from one place to another

bits of rock broken off from a larger rock by weathering

the dropping of rocks and sediment in a new place

rock formed from heat and pressure deep in the earth, or from chemical changes

all the changes that rock keeps going through

the breaking down of rock by natural forces such as wind, rain, and ice

fossil	decay
fossilization	mold
preserved	cast
dissolve	trace fossil
impression	fossil record

to rot

the remains or traces of an ancient plant or animal

the hollow shape of a plant or animal left in rock

the process of forming a fossil

a fossil that forms when minerals fill a mold

kept whole

the marks made by the movement of an ancient animal

to break down and wash away

all the fossils taken together, showing the history of life on Earth in ages past

an image pressed into matter

mineral	cleavage
inorganic	streak
element	luster
compound	metallic
crystal	nonmetallic

the quality of some minerals to split along a smooth inner surface, or plane

an inorganic solid that is formed naturally in the earth

the color of the powder left when a mineral is scratched on a special white plate

having no living matter

the shine or lack of shine of a mineral's surface

a mineral made up of only one type of matter

having a shiny luster like a metal

a mineral made of two or more elements

not having the shiny luster of a metal

a regular, repeating shape with smooth sides

natural resource

conservation

inexhaustible resource

recycling

renewable resource

preservation

nonrenewable resource

pollutant

fossil fuel

acid rain

the protection of natural resources by using less of them

something found in nature that people use

using materials from used goods to make new goods

a resource that can be used over and over without being used up

the protection of natural resources by not using them or by keeping them clean

a resource that can be replaced as it is used

a chemical from human activities that harms natural resources

a resource that cannot be replaced once it is used up

a pollutant made up of rainwater and acid from factory smoke

an energy source that began forming millions of years ago from decaying plants and animals

atmosphere	stratosphere
troposphere	ozone layer
water vapor	mesosphere
nitrogen	thermosphere
oxygen	exosphere

the layer of atmosphere above
the troposphere

all the air, or mixture of gases,
that surrounds Earth

a thin layer in the stratosphere that
contains a type of oxygen that
absorbs harmful rays of the sun

the layer of atmosphere closest to
Earth's surface

the layer of atmosphere above
the stratosphere

water in the form of a gas

the layer of atmosphere above
the mesosphere

a common gas that makes up about
78% of the air in the troposphere

the top and widest layer of the
atmosphere

a common gas that makes up about
21% of the air in the troposphere

©Curriculum Associates, LLC *Passwords: Science Vocabulary, Earth Science, Lesson 9—Word Cards*

evaporation	runoff
humidity	watershed
condensation	groundwater
precipitation	aquifer
surface water	water table

surface water that flows along on top of the land

the changing from a liquid to a gas

the area of land drained by a river and the streams that flow into the river

the amount of water vapor in the air

water that is beneath Earth's surface

the changing form a gas to a liquid

a layer of rock that fills with groundwater

water falling to Earth as a liquid or solid

the height of groundwater under the ground

water at Earth's surface

 Passwords: Science Vocabulary, Earth Science, Lesson 10—Word Cards

ocean floor	abyssal plain
continental shelf	seamount
continental slope	oceanic ridge
submarine canyon	trench
continental rise	subduction zone

the fairly level ocean floor between the continental rise and mid-ocean

the land under the oceans

a volcanic mountain that forms on the ocean floor

the land at the edge of a continent that gently slopes underwater

a long chain of mountains on the ocean floor that forms where two plates are moving apart

the steeply sloping part of the ocean floor between the continental shelf and the continental rise

a very deep, wide valley that forms at a subduction zone on the ocean floor

a deep underwater valley with sharp sides that forms on the continental slope

an area where one plate of the ocean floor is sliding under another plate

the sloping part of the ocean floor between the continental slope and the abyssal plain

climate

cumulus clouds

air mass

air pressure

front

westerlies

cirrus clouds

trade winds

stratus clouds

jet stream

puffy white clouds that extend upward from low to mid-height above Earth's surface

the average weather of a region over a long period of time

the force of air pushing down on Earth

a huge body of air with the same features throughout, such as temperature and moisture

large belts of winds that blow west to east

where the edges of two air masses meet

two belts of winds above and below the equator that mostly blow east to west

high, thin, icy clouds

a narrow band of very strong winds that blow west to east

low gray clouds that often bring steady rain

 Passwords: Science Vocabulary, Earth Science, Lesson 12—Word Cards

solar system	asteroid
gravity	comet
inner planets	galaxy
satellite	light-year
outer planets	universe

a small, solid object of rock and metal orbiting the sun

the sun and all the planets and other objects that orbit the sun

a ball of rock, dust, and ice that orbits the sun in a huge oval and displays a tail of glowing gases when it travels close to the sun

the force of attraction between all objects

a large group of stars, planets, moons, asteroids, comets, dust, and gas held together by gravity

the four planets of the solar system that orbit closest to the sun

the distance light can travel in a year

a moon or object orbiting around a planet

all the energy and matter that exists

the planets of the solar system that orbit farthest from the sun

nebula	supernova
red giant	neutron star
white dwarf	pulsar
nova	black hole
blue giant	supergiant

a huge explosion that occurs when a large star called a supergiant collapses suddenly

a huge cloud of dust and gas in space

a tiny, rapidly spinning star made from a very dense core of matter

a cool but fairly bright, large red star

as observed from Earth, a neutron star that gives off evenly spaced pulses of energy, so its energy seems to blink

a very small, dense white star that forms from the collapse of a red giant

a region of extremely dense matter with such a strong pull of gravity that light cannot escape

the sudden, strong brightening, for a time, of a white dwarf

a very large, very bright star

a huge, bright, very hot star

revolution	phase
rotation	waxing
axis	waning
tilt	lunar eclipse
tides	solar eclipse

the changing pattern of light on the moon as seen from Earth

the movement of one object in space around another object

the growing larger of the lighted part of the moon that is seen from Earth

the spinning of an object on its axis

the growing smaller of the lighted part of the moon that is seen from Earth

an imaginary line around which an object rotates

the blocking of the sun's light from reaching the moon by Earth when Earth moves between the full moon and the sun

the slant of an object's axis

the blocking of the sun's light from reaching places on Earth by the moon when the new moon moves between Earth and the sun

the daily rise and fall of the level of the ocean

 Passwords: Science Vocabulary, Earth Science, Lesson 15—Word Cards